D1646044

THE CESSNA 150
A PILOTS GUIDE

JEREMY M. PRATT

First Edition 1993

Copyright © 1993 Airplan Flight Equipment & JEREMY M. PRATT

THE CESSNA 150 A PILOTS GUIDE
JEREMY M. PRATT

ISBN: 1 874783 25 X

Airplan Flight Equipment, Southside, Manchester International Airport, Wilmslow, Cheshire SK9 4LL, U.K.   Tel: 061-499 0023   Fax: 061-499 0298

Acknowledgments

I would like to thank all those whose knowledge, help and advice went into this book, in particular :

Farooq Ahmed

CAA Safety Promotion Section

Colourmatch

Cheshire Air Training School

Deltair

Adrian Dickinson

Steve Dickinson

George Firbank

East Midlands Flying School

Peggy Follis

David Hockings

Andy Holland

Light Planes (Lancs) Ltd

Luton Flight Training

Manchester School of Flying

Steve Maffitt

Chris Nolan

Andy Parker

Ravenair

Neil Rigby

Ian Sixsmith

John Thorpe

Visual Eyes

Sarah, Kate and Miles

Jeremy M Pratt
June 1993

Contents

Section 1 – General Description

Section 2 – Limitations

© Airplan Flight Equipment 1993

Section 3 – Handling the Cessna 150

Section 4 – Mixture and Carb Icing Supplement

Section 5 – Expanded Cessna 150 Pre-Flight Check List

Section 6 – Cessna Loading and Performance

Section 7 – Conversions

THIS AFE PILOT GUIDE IS NOT AN AUTHORITATIVE DOCUMENT AND SHOULD NOT BE TAKEN AS SUCH

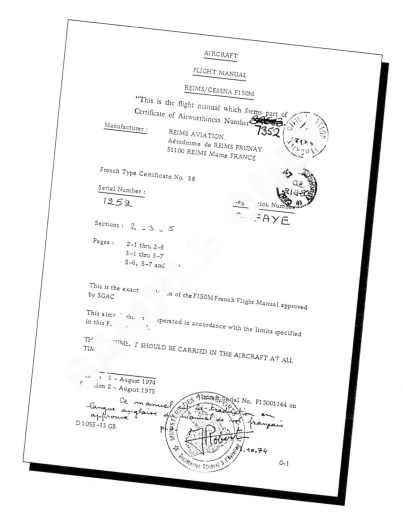

The approved Pilot Operating Handbook/Flight Manual (illustrated above), as amended, is the only source of authoritative information. Each individual aircraft has its own individual POH/FM, in the interests of safety & good airmanship the pilot should be familiar with this document.

The Cessna 150

In the late 1950's Cessna looked to build a two place trainer based on the successful 120/140 series that had been in production since 1948, but incorporating many of the design features of the newly launched 172.

The Cessna 150 entered production in 1959, and as with all subsequent marks was powered by a Continental O-200-A engine developing 100HP. The launch of the new aircraft gave the Cessna marketing people a field day, and like its stablemate - the 172 - the Cessna 150 came to be burdened with such timeless phrases as 'Land-O-Matic' landing gear, 'Para-Lift' flaps and 'Omni-Vision' windows.

This publication covers the 150 from the 1966 'F' model through to the last 150s ('M' model) produced in 1977, when the 150 was replaced by the Lycoming powered 152. The 1966 model introduced several new features over previous models, notably a swept fin, electric flaps and a pneumatic reed stall warner. The 1967 'G' featured a widened cabin and an alternator replaced the generator previously used. In the 1969 'J' models the electrical system was further revised to incorporate

Early 150 cockpits have a dated, almost vintage look (1967 C150).

'Rocker' switches rather than the 'Push/Pull' toggle switches. In 1970 (K model) 'conical cambered' wingtips were introduced, which improved low speed handling. Also in this year the 150 Aerobat version was introduced (designation A150). This version was stressed to +6g and -3g allowing a full range of aerobatics to be flown. Further refinements continued through the 1970s. The 1975 'M' models had a larger fin, and the 'Commuter II' option was introduced offering an up graded avionics package. In 1976 circuit breakers were fitted in preference to fuses, and in its last year of production (1977) the 150 was given a pre-selectable flap setting switch - an improvement far more significant in practice than in writing.

In addition to the aircraft produced in the USA nearly 2000 150s were built in Reims, France. These aircraft are mostly identical to the USA production, but carry the prefix 'F' eg F150J, FA150 Aerobat.

In total almost 24000 150s were built, not quite a record but certainly a most significant contribution to the ranks of training aircraft still in service today. Over 30 years after its inception it is rare to visit a busy training airfield and not find a 150 somewhere around.

Although the 'Aerobat' models are not specifically described in this publication, most of the information is relevant to the Aerobat. As always the Aircraft Flight Manual is the authoritative document.

Model Numbers and Production Years

PRODUCTION YEAR	MODEL	MODEL NAME
1966	150 F	Cessna 150 *
1967	150 G	Cessna 150 *
1968	150 H	Cessna 150 *
1969	150 J	Cessna 150 *
1969	F150J	Reims 150*
1970	150 K	Cessna 150 *
1970	F150K	Reims/Cessna F150*
1970	A150 K	Cessna 150K Aerobat
1970	FA150K	Reims/Cessna F150 Aerobat
1971 - 1974	150 L	Cessna 150 *
1971 - 1974	F150L	Reims/Cessna F150*
1975 - 1977	150 M	Cessna 150 *
1975 - 1977	F150 M	Reims/Cessna F150*

* available as Standard - virtually without instruments on delivery
Trainer - with standard instrument and radio fit
Commuter - upgraded avionics fit

PRODUCTION YEAR	MODEL	MODEL NAME
1971 - 1974	A150 L	Cessna 150L Aerobat
1971 - 1974	FA150L	Reims/Cessna F150 Aerobat
1975 - 1977	A150 M	Cessna 150M Aerobat
1975 - 1977	FA150 M	Reims/Cessna F150 Aerobat

FRA150 Aerobat with distinctive 'chequered' paint scheme.

A small number of Reims built Aerobats, fitted with a Rolls Royce 0-240 engine, are designated FRA - eg FRA150 M Aerobat.

The Cessna 150

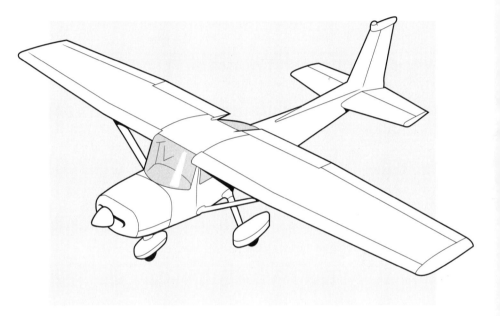

General Description

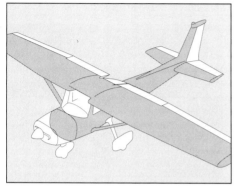

The Airframe

The Cessna 150 airframe can be described as being of all metal construction, the primary structure being constructed of aluminium alloy. Some non-structural components such as the wing tips, tailplane tips and wing strut fairings are made from GRP.

The fuselage has a semi-monocoque structure, that is the vertical bulkheads and fraames, horizontal stringers and reinforcing channels run the length of the fuselage. The metal skin is rivetted to this structure. This arrangement is conventional for modern light aircraft and allows loads to be spread over the whole construction. At the rear of the fuselage the tail unit consists of a swept fin with rudder and conventional tailplane with elevators. Underneath the rear fuselage a metal loop tie down point/tail

guard is fitted. This metal loop should be carefully checked for damage during the pre-flight inspection. It is possible for a 'tail-strike' on take off or landing to push back this loop far enough to restrict the movement of the rudder. Small drain holes are drilled in the underneath fuselage and at the base of the rudder. If it is suspected that water has collected in the rear fuselage the tail can be lowered, allowing the water to drain out through these holes.

The tail tie down loop under the tail unit.

The wings are of semi-cantilever design (supported by an external strut) and have a 1° dihedral. At the top of each strut a metal ring is fitted to be used as a tie down point. Up to 1970 models standard wing tips are fitted. From 1970 models on conical cambered wing tips are fitted, which apparently improve slow speed handling.

The wings are supported by an external strut and have just 1° of dihedral.

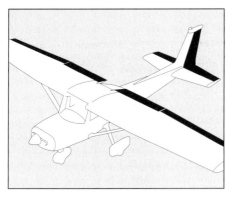

The Flying Controls

Dual flight controls are fitted as standard and link the cockpit controls to the control surface via cable linkages.

The AILERONS are of the differential frise type, moving upward through 20° and downward through 14°. Balance weights are incorporated at the lower inner edge of the ailerons.

The FLAPS are slotted and incorporate a Fowler action over the first 10°, they are electrically operated, and can be set between 0° and 40°.

The cockpit control lock fixes the elevators and ailerons in position. When properly fitted the label should cover the magneto switch and master switch.

Flaps at 40°, clearly showing the 'slot' design.

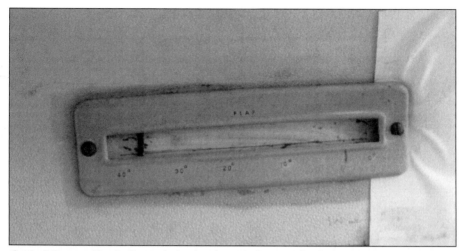

Cockpit flap position indicator hole showing 40° flap set. On this early 150 the indicator is located above the left door.

The flap switch is to the right of the mixture control. To lower flap the lever is moved down, whilst checking the flap position indicator on the left cabin wall. On the very late 150s (1977 model) a pre-selectable flap control is incorporated. This control is gated in 10° stages and a small indicator next to the lever shows the actual flap movement. The flap system occasionally suffers from switching problems, these problems can lead to stuck or jammed flaps, or the flaps moving from the position set by the pilot.

The RUDDER is operated from the rudder pedals (which are also linked to the steerable nose wheel) and can move through 23° either side of the neutral position. On the trailing edge of the control surface a ground adjustable trim tab is fitted, a horn balance is incorporated in the upper forward portion of the control surface (ahead of the hinge line). From 1975 models on the fin and rudder area is increased slightly, which gives cleaner spin entries and recoveries.

The ELEVATORS are fitted to the tailplane, and move up through 25° (23° 1975 models and on) and down through 15°. They incorporate a horn balance at their outer forward edge ahead of the hinge line.

An adjustable TRIM TAB is fitted to the right hand elevator. Operation of the cockpit trim wheel (located below the throttle) moves this control surface independently of the elevator control. The trim tab moves through 10° up and 20° down. An indicator mounted next to the cockpit trim wheel shows the trim position set, and the control works in the natural sense, ie trimming the wheel forward gives nose down trim and vice versa.

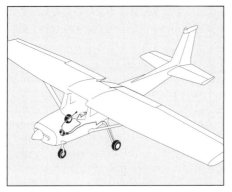

The Undercarriage

The 150 undercarriage is fixed and of the tricycle type. The main gear is a flat steel spring through to 1970 models, and tubular steel undercarriage legs from 1971 models on. The tubular leg is surrounded by a full length fairing, both types are fitted with a step. The main gear attaches to the lower fuselage, with a plastic fairing where the leg joins the lower fuselage surface.

The main gear has an 6' 6" track (flat steel spring gear) or 7' 7" track (tubular steel leg).

The 'tubular' main gear leg fitted to 1971 and later models.

The 'flat spring' main undercarriage leg of pre-1971 models.

The nose gear attaches to the engine mount and has an air/oil oleo strut to damp and absorb the normal operating loads. On the rear of the nose leg a torque link is fitted to maintain the correct alignment of the nose wheel, its lower arm is fitted to the nose wheel fork and the upper arm to the oleo cylinder casing. Also fitted to the nose leg is a small cylinder-piston unit, the shimmy damper. The purpose of this unit is to reduce nose wheel shimmy (rapid oscillation of the nose wheel, felt as vibration through the rudder pedals) which is most prevalent during take off and landing.

Nose undercarriage with shimmy damper.

© Airplan Flight Equipment 1993

The nose gear is steerable through a spring linkage to the rudder pedals, it is steerable through approx 10° either side of neutral, and can castor under differential braking up to 30°

The braking system consists of single disc brake assemblies fitted to the main undercarriage and operated by a hydraulic system. The brakes are operated through the upper portion of each rudder pedal. The pilot's (left hand side) toe brakes have a separate brake cylinder above each pedal, and it is possible to operate the brakes differentially - to the left or right wheel. Where the right side pedals are also fitted with toe brakes they are mechanically linked to the pilot side brake cylinders. The system of toe brakes allows the aircraft to turn in a very tight circle, and it is possible to lock one main wheel with the use of some toe brake force. Turning around a wheel in this fashion is not recommended as it tends to 'scrub' the tyre and put excessive pressure on the tyre side walls.

A parking brake control is fitted on the far left side of the instrument panel. To operate the parking brake the brake pedals are both depressed, and the parking brake knob is pulled out, the pedal pressure is then relaxed and the parking brake control released. The parking brake control is attached to a locking plate, which traps pressure in the system whilst the toe brakes are being activated. The problem is that there is no obvious visual check to show the pilot that the brakes are applied. When the aircraft has been parked it is common practice to try moving the aircraft, to ensure that the parking brake is applied.

Problems can arise through the amount of force applied by the pilot to operate the brakes, especially when applying the parking brake. If excessive force is used over a period of time it can lead to fatigue cracks and failures of the rudder bars and seat frames. There have been several reported rudder pedal failures on 150s, as well as seat failures (see Seats and Harnesses).

The main wheels are fitted with 600 X 6 tyres as standard, the nose wheel with 500 X 5. To be serviceable the tyre grooves should have at least 2mm depth over at least 75% of the tyre circumference. Additionally there should be no point on the tyre at which the tread across the width of the tyre has been worn to less that 2mm (as might happen if the tyre had been 'flat spotted' in a skid).

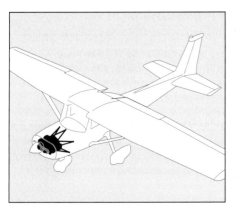

The Engine

The 150 is fitted with a Continental 0-200-A engine giving 100 HP at 2750 RPM.

The engine is a four cylinder unit, with cylinders horizontally opposed across the crankshaft. The cylinders are staggered so that each connecting rod has its own crankshaft throw, the cylinder heads and crankcase assembly are fashioned from aluminium alloy castings.

The engine is air cooled. Airflow enters the engine compartment at the front of the cowling, and is directed by baffles to flow over the whole engine. Th steel cylinders feature deep fins to aid cooling, the airflow leaves the engine compartment at the lower aft cowling underneath the engine compartment.

The engine is attached to the steel tubular engine mounting with rubber and metal shock mounts to reduce engine vibration. The engine mount attaches to the firewall.

Some Reims built Aerobats are fitted with a Rolls Royce 0-240 engine, rated at 130 HP at 2800 RPM. These aircraft have an increased maximum gross weight (1650 lbs) and different airspeed limitations and performance figures to standard Aerobats. Several operators have removed this engine and replaced it with a standard 0-200 engine.

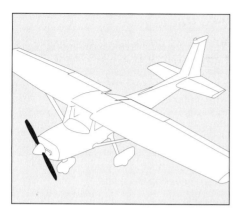

The Propeller

The propeller is an all metal, two bladed, fixed pitch design, turned by direct drive from the engine crankshaft. The propeller rotates clockwise as seen from the cockpit. The diameter is 69". Differing shape long and short spinners are fitted to various models of the 150. The long spinner adds 9" to the length of the aircraft.

The propeller of a 150 Aerobat.

The Ignition System

The engine features a dual ignition system, fitted with two magnetos. The magnetos are small electrical AC generators which are driven by the crankshaft rotation to provide a very high voltage to a distributor, which directs it via high voltage leads (or high tension leads) to the spark plugs. At the spark plug the current must cross a gap, in doing so a spark is produced which ignites the fuel/air mixture in the cylinder.

The magnetos are fitted at the rear of the engine, one each side of the engine centre line (hence Left and Right magnetos). Each cylinder has two spark plugs (top and bottom) for safety and efficiency, each magneto fires one spark plug in each cylinder. The leads that run from the magnetos to the spark plugs should be secure and there should be no splits or cracks in the plastic insulation covering the leads.

It is worth emphasising that the ignition system is totally independent of the aircraft electrical system, and once the engine is running it will operate regardless of the serviceability of the battery or alternator.

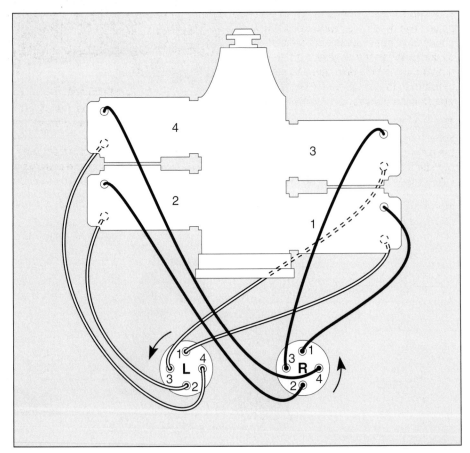

The Oil System

The oil system of the engine provides for lubrication, cooling, sealing, cleansing and protection against corrosion. The system is a wet-sump, system, the oil sump is located under the engine, and oil is drawn from here through a screen and to the engine driven oil pump. From here the oil is fed into the left oil gallery, via the optional oil cooler, across the crankshaft to the right oil gallery and to the pressure relief valve. Throughout the engine, oil drains down to the sump by gravity.

Oil contents can be checked on a dipstick on the right side of the engine which is accessible from the cowling inspection hatch. The dipstick is graduated in US quarts and measures the contents in the oil sump. When the engine has been running, the oil will take up to 10 minutes to return to the sump, and only then can a true reading be taken.

With the cowling hatch open, the oil dipstick can be checked (lower right).

The oil temperature gauge in the cockpit senses oil temperature just downstream of the oil pump before it enters the engine. The instrument is connected to a temperature bulb by a capillary tube. The system is filled with fluid, whose expansion and contraction with temperature is measured on the instrument gauge.

The oil pressure gauge reads from a direct pressure pick up point just before the pressure relief valve.

The Starter System

The starter motor is housed at the lower front left side of the engine. It incorporates a geared cog that engages on to the teeth of the starter ring when the key starter is operated. As the engine is turned an impulse coupling in each magneto operates, this retards the spark and aids starting. When the engine fires and begins to rotate under its own power this impulse coupling ceases to operate and normal spark timing is resumed. When the key starter is released, allowing the key to return to the 'BOTH' position, the cog on the starter motor withdraws to be clear of the starter ring.

A STARTER WARNING LIGHT is fitted in the cockpit. This illuminates when the starter is operated to show that the starter motor is engaging the starter ring. When the key starter is released the light should go out. If the light remains on this means that the starter motor is still engaged to the starter ring. In this instance the starter motor is being turned by the engine, and serious damage may be caused to the aircraft electrical system, in this case the engine should be shut down immediately.

If the starter warning light remains on after starting the engine should be shut down.

The Fuel System

The 150 has a simple gravity feed fuel system.

There are two aluminium fuel tanks, located one in each wing and joined by a balance pipe. From each tank a fuel line runs down the inner fuselage to the fuel shut off valve, on to the fuel strainer and to the carburettor. A separate line runs from the strainer bowl to the cockpit primer and from there to the engine intake manifold.

When checking fuel contents before flight it is VITAL to check fuel contents VISUALLY, the cockpit fuel gauges are not accurate enough to assess true fuel contents. When the fuel contents have been visually checked care must be taken to replace the fuel caps securely. If the caps are loose or cross-threaded fuel may vent out from the tank during flight.

The high wing Cessna singles feature in accidents caused by fuel exhaustion. Often the fuel tanks were NOT visually checked during the pre-flight checks, and the fuel ran out even though the gauges were indicating that sufficient fuel remained. The 150 is not unique in having fuel exhaustion accidents. However its high wing design can lead to a reluctance by the pilot to climb up and visually check the contents. It is for this reason that some the 150s are fitted with a step on each wing strut and a grab handle on each side of the upper cowling to aid access to the upper wing.

When the fuel tank levels are low, say below 1/4 full, prolonged sideslip or skidding manoeuvres should be avoided as the tank outlet may be uncovered, and the fuel supply interrupted. For the same reason extreme 'running' take offs should also be avoided.

In a gravity feed system positive tank venting is of vital importance. The left tank has a TANK VENT, this is a forward facing pipe on the lower inboard surface of the left wing which extends into the left fuel tank. The pipe is located directly behind the wing strut to protect it from icing. The function of this pipe is to maintain ambient pressure above the fuel in the fuel tank. As the vent pipe alone cannot always guarantee proper venting, most 150s are now fitted with vented fuel caps in addition. Should the vents become blocked a depression will form in the tank as the fuel level lowers and fuel flow to the engine may be interrupted.

During the pre-flight inspection it is essential to visually check the fuel contents.

There are three FUEL STRAINERS, one at the lower rear inboard edge of each tank, accessible from the inboard lower wing surface, and one located at the fuel strainer bowl. The tank fuel strainers can be used with a fuel tester to collect a fuel sample from each tank. The fuel bowl is located at the firewall, its strainer is operated by a control located under the right cowling inspection flap. When this control is operated (by pulling) fuel will run from a pipe in the region of the nose leg. To collect fuel from this pipe whilst operating the drainer can be difficult, but it should not be allowed to merely run onto the ground, as water or contaminated fuel could go undetected. It is imperative to ensure that the fuel strainer control is returned to the OFF position after use, or fuel may continue to drain from the pipe out of view of the pilot.

The fuel shutoff valve is located on the cockpit floor between the forward edges of the seats. The lever is normally in the ON position, lying horizontally. In the event of an emergency requiring the fuel to be turned off, the lever is moved to the vertically up position, turning the fuel OFF. In the past it had been common practice to safety wire the lever in the ON position. This is now discouraged and pilots are advised to periodically operate the lever (NOT in flight !) to ensure it moves freely.

The pipe running from the fuel strainer.

The fuel shut off valve ahead of the seats.

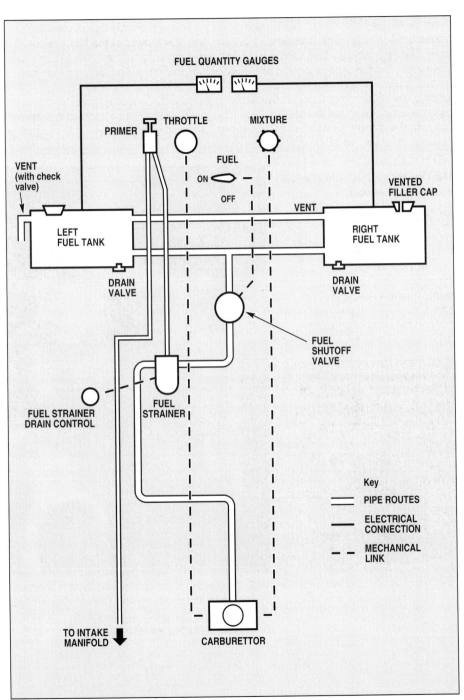

FUEL QUANTITY GAUGES

PRIMER   THROTTLE   MIXTURE

FUEL
ON   OFF

VENT (with check valve)

VENTED FILLER CAP

VENT

LEFT FUEL TANK   RIGHT FUEL TANK

DRAIN VALVE   DRAIN VALVE

FUEL SHUTOFF VALVE

FUEL STRAINER DRAIN CONTROL   FUEL STRAINER

Key
PIPE ROUTES
ELECTRICAL CONNECTION
MECHANICAL LINK

TO INTAKE MANIFOLD   CARBURETTOR

The Carburettor

The carburettor mixes air with fuel from the fuel system and supplies the fuel/air mix to the intake manifold and from there to the individual cylinder intake pipes. The up-draft carburettor is located under the engine, and takes induction air from a scoop intake in the lower front cowling. This air is filtered and then fed into the carburettor air box. In this box a butterfly valve is used to allow either the cold air, or heated air, to be fed to the carburettor. Heated air comes from an unfiltered inlet in the front cowling baffle which then passes into a shroud around the exhaust which heats it before it reaches the carburettor. Hot or cold air is selected via the carburettor heat control in the cockpit, the use of this control and the subject of carburettor icing are discussed fully later in this book.

An ACCELERATOR PUMP is fitted to the carburettor. With a standard carburettor when the throttle is opened suddenly it is possible for a momentarily lean mixture to occur, this causes the engine to hesitate, often at an inopportune moment. The accelerator pump is designed to enrich the mixture momentarily when the throttle is opened suddenly and so prevent any engine hesitation.

With the cowling removed the carburettor is clearly visible under the engine behind the air intake filter. If the throttle is 'pumped', raw fuel drips from the carburettor, creating a fire risk.

The PRIMER control is situated on the far left of the instrument panel under the parking brake, and is used as an aid to starting. The control is unlocked by rotating the control until a pin on the shaft aligns with the cut out in the collar. The control can then be pulled out, filling the pump with fuel from the fuel strainer. The primer is then pushed in, delivering fuel to the engine intake manifold. When priming is completed the primer should be pushed fully in with the pin aligned with the cut out in the collar, then rotated about half a turn to lock the primer. As a check, attempt to pull the primer out, it should remain locked. It is important that the primer is fully locked, as if it is not, engine rough running may result.

The MIXTURE is controlled from the mixture knob located on the lower instrument panel, which adjusts the fuel/air ratio in the carburettor. The mixture control may be a simple push/pull type, or of the vernier type. The vernier type of control is moved by depressing a button in the centre of the control and moving the control in or out. For fine adjustment the control can be rotated clockwise to richen the mixture, and anti-clockwise to lean the mixture. In the fully forward position it gives a RICH mixture, and if moved to the rearward ICO (Idle Cut Off) position the fuel supply is cut off and the engine stops.

The THROTTLE is located to the left of the mixture control, it is also of a push/pull type, but does not have the vernier fine adjustment feature described above. The throttle does have a friction nut at the point where it joins the instrument panel, when this nut is rotated clockwise the throttle movement becomes more difficult, when rotated anti-clockwise the throttle movement becomes loose.

The throttle friction nut is clearly visible. This 1967 C150 also has old style push/pull electrical switches.

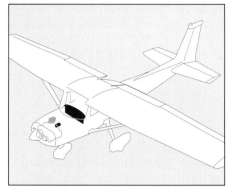

The Electrical System

The 150 has a 14 volt, direct current electrical system. An alternator is mounted to the rear face of the engine and is engine driven, the alternator is rated at 60 amps, (up to 1967, 150s are fitted with a 35 amp generator). A 12 volt battery is located inside a vented box on the upper forward right side of the firewall, the battery capacity is approx. 25 ampere hours.

The ALTERNATOR is the primary source of power to the electrical system in normal operations with the engine running. The alternator produces alternating current (AC) which is converted into direct current (DC) by diodes incorporated in the alternator housing which act as rectifiers. By their design alternators require a small voltage (about 3 volts) to produce the electromagnetic field required inside the alternator. The significance of this is that if the battery is completely discharged (flat), the alternator will not be able to supply any power to the electrical system, even after the engine has been started by some other means (ie external power or hand swinging). Output from the alternator is controlled by a VOLTAGE REGULATOR mounted on the left side of the firewall. From 1972 models on an OVERVOLTAGE SENSOR protects the system from possible damage due to an over-voltage condition. In the event of a high voltage a relay opens isolating the alternator from the electrical system.

The primary purpose of the BATTERY is to provide power for engine starting, the initial excitation of the alternator and as a backup in the event of alternator failure. In normal operations with the engine running the alternator provides the power to the electrical system and charges the battery. A fully charged battery has a charging current of about 2 amperes, in a partially discharged condition (ie just after engine start) the charging rate can be much higher than this. In the event of an alternator failure the battery is providing ALL power to the electrical system. In theory a fully charged 25 ampere hour battery is capable of providing 25 amps for 1 hour, or 1 amp for 25 hours, or 12.5 amps for 2 hours etc. In practice the power available is governed by factors such as battery age and condition, load placed on it etc. The best advice is to reduce electrical load to the minimum consistent with safety and plan to make a landing at the earliest opportunity.

With the cowlings removed, the battery can be seen, at the lower fire wall.

The AMMETER indicates in amperes the electrical current flowing to or from the battery. In normal operations with the engine running the ammeter will indicate the charging rate of the battery. Should the alternator fail or be shut down the ammeter will show a discharge, the amount of current flowing from the battery to the electrical system.

On 1972 models and on a red 'HIGH VOLTAGE' warning light is fitted, linked to the over-voltage sensor. Should an over-voltage condition lead to the sensor shutting down the alternator, the high voltage light will illuminate to indicate that the battery is supplying all electrical power; in addition the ammeter will show a discharge. A red 'LOW VOLTAGE' warning light may also be fitted. Should the voltage fall below a pre set level the low voltage light will illuminate to indicate a drain on the battery and the ammeter will show a discharge. It is not unusual for the low voltage light to flicker at low RPMs, especially during taxying. When a higher RPM is set the light should go out again.

With the alternator 'off-line', the battery is supplying all power to the electrical system. The high voltage light has illuminated and the ammeter is showing a discharge.

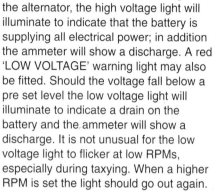

The old style on/off master switch.

The pilot controls the electrical system via the 'MASTER SWITCH' located on the left side of the instrument panel. From 1970 models on this switch is a split rocker having two halves, labelled 'BAT' and 'ALT' and normally the switch is operated as one, both halves being used together. The 'BAT' half of the switch can be operated independently, so that all electrical power is being drawn from the battery only.

However the 'ALT' side can only be turned on in conjunction with the 'BAT' half, for the reasons covered previously. Should an electrical problem occur the MASTER SWITCH can be used to reset the electrical system by turning it OFF for 2 seconds and then turning it ON again. On pre 1970 models the switch is not split and can only be used as one.

The 'split rocker switch' type master switch.

The external power receptacle, behind a door in the left side front fuselage.

As an option the aircraft may be fitted with an EXTERNAL POWER RECEPTACLE, which can be used to connect external power for starting or operation of the aircraft electrical system. Before using external power it is imperative to check that the external power unit is of the correct voltage - otherwise SERIOUS DAMAGE COULD BE INFLICTED ON THE ELECTRICAL SYSTEM. Additionally it should be remembered that if the battery is totally flat (completely discharged), it will need to be removed and recharged or replaced before flight. Cessna recommend that the master switch be turned ON before connecting the external power source, so that any transient voltages can be absorbed by the battery.

The various electrically operated systems are protected by individual FUSES up until 1975 models, thereafter CIRCUIT BREAKERS replace the fuses. With the fuse system spare fuses are located in the door of the glove compartment. The fuses show their ratings, of course a 'blown' fuse should only be replaced with a fuse of the same rating. With a circuit breaker system, should a problem (ie a short circuit) occur the relevant circuit breaker may 'pop', and will be seen to be raised in relation to the other circuit breakers (CBs). The correct procedure is to allow the CB to cool for, say, 2 minutes, then reset it and check the result. If the CB pops again it should not be reset. The alternator field circuit has a 5 ampere CB, which automatically resets. All CB's show their rating and the components they protect.

Apart from engine starting and alternator field the electrical system supplies power to the following:

ALL internal and external lights.
ALL radios and intercom.
Wing flaps, pitot heater
Turn coordinator.
Fuel gauges.

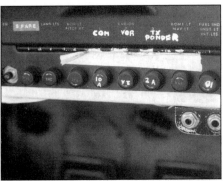

Fuses marked with their ratings. Spare fuses are in the glove compartment above.

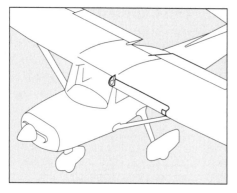

The Stall Warner System

An intake in the left wing leading edge gives an aural stall warning through a horn above the left fresh air control in the cockpit. When the stalling angle of attack is approached the airflow over the leading edge causes a suction through the reed producing a loud tone, which becomes increasingly high pitched as the stalling angle of attack is reached. Typically the stall warner activates 5 - 10 Kts above the stall speed.

To check the function of the stall warner on the ground the intake should be checked for blockages, and a suction can be applied by sucking air through the intake. If this is done it is recommended that a handkerchief or something similar be placed over the intake first, to avoid the unpleasant possibility of swallowing any insects stuck in the intake.

The stall warner intake in the leading edge of the left wing leading edge.

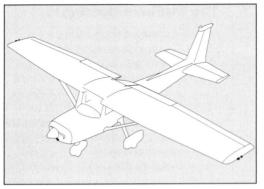

The Lighting System

The 150 may be equipped with a variety of optional internal and external lighting. As a general rule wing tip strobes, where fitted, are not used during taxying as they can dazzle and distract those nearby, they are however very effective in the air. If flying in cloud conditions or heavy precipitation it is recommended that they be turned off as the pilot may become spatially disoriented. The landing light and taxy lights are fitted in the left wing leading edge, up until 1970 models, after which they are fitted in the lower front engine cowl. Again they should be used with some discretion, not least because of the very short life of the lamp bulbs. There is also an overhead 'dome' light located in the cabin ceiling, this light is of a set brightness and has an on/off switch located on its side.

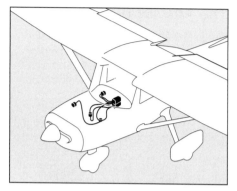

The Vacuum System

An engine driven vacuum pump is mounted below the front of the engine. This pump is fitted with a plastic shear drive, so that should the pump seize, the drive will shear and the engine will not be damaged. The air enters the suction system through a filter, passes through the air-driven gyro instruments (and is measured for the suction gauge), flows through a vacuum regulator and into the vacuum pump, from which it is expelled through a short pipe.

Suction is used to drive the gyros in the Attitude Indicator (or Artificial Horizon) and Heading Indicator (or Direction Indicator). A suction gauge mounted on the instrument panel measures suction, for cruising RPMs and altitudes the reading should be between 4.6 and 5.4 inches of mercury. At higher or lower suction the gyros may become unreliable. A lower suction over an extended period may indicate a faulty vacuum regulator,dirty screens or a system leak. If the vacuum pump fails or a line collapses the suction gauge reading will fall to zero, and the Attitude Indicator and Heading Indicator will become unreliable over a period of some minutes as the gyros run down losing RPM. The real danger here is that the effect is gradual and may not be noticed by the pilot for some time.

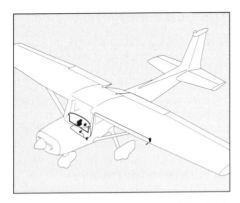

The Pitot-Static System

The pitot-static system supplies static pressure to the Vertical Speed Indicator (VSI) and Altimeter, and static and pitot pressure to the Airspeed Indicator (ASI).

The pitot head located under the left wing.

Pitot pressure comes from a PITOT HEAD which is located under the left wing. Static pressure comes from a STATIC VENT located on the forward left fuselage .

No checking system is incorporated in the system, and instrument indications in the event of a leak or blockage are outside of the scope of this book. As an option the pitot head may have a heating element which is activated by a switch labelled 'PITOT HEAT'. Pitot heat can prevent blockage of the pitot head in heavy rain or icing, this notwithstanding it must be remembered that the 150 IS NOT CLEARED FOR FLIGHT INTO KNOWN ICING CONDITIONS.

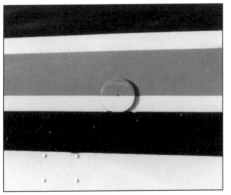

The static vent on the left forward fuselage.

The 150 is not fitted with an alternate static source, so the pressure instruments may become unusable if the normal static vent is blocked. In this instance it is possible to smash the face of the VSI, allowing static pressure from the cabin to enter the system. It should be emphasised that this action is rather drastic (and expensive) and will probably require the use of the blunt end of the fire extinguisher. Action of this type should only be used in a genuine emergency.

The external static vent should be checked before flight to ensure that it is clear and unobstructed. A similar check is carried out on the pitot head, which may be protected on the ground with a removable pitot cover. It is important not to blow into either pitot or static vent, doing so can result in damage to the pressure instruments.

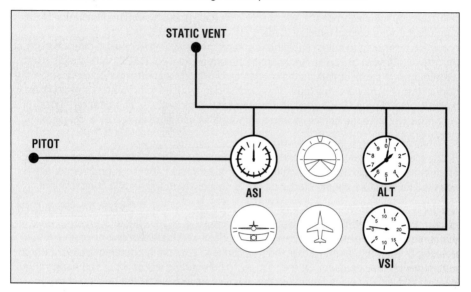

The Heating and Ventilation System

Cabin heating is supplied via a muffler around the engine exhaust system. This allows air which has entered from an engine baffle inlet to be warmed by the exhaust pipes, it is then directed to outlets in the footwells and at the lower windscreen a single defrosting outlet is fitted on the left side of the upper glareshield. The heating is controlled from a control labelled 'CABIN HT' mounted next to the flap control. This control is pulled out to select cabin heat and pushed fully in to close the shut off valve at the firewall. Next to the cabin heat control, a control labelled 'CABIN AIR' directs fresh air through the same outlets as the heated air. Pulling this control out opens a small door in the right forward fuselage. This control can be used individually, or more often to blend with the heated air to provide a comfortable temperature. The heating system is very effective once the engine is warm, although its use is governed by a couple of safety factors:

Firstly the heating system effectively opens a path through the firewall between the engine compartment and the cockpit. For this reason the cabin heat and defrost are selected OFF before engine start, or if fire is suspected in the engine compartment.

Secondly with a system of this type there is always a danger of Carbon Monoxide (CO) being introduced into the cabin. Carbon Monoxide is a gas produced as a by product of the combustion process. It is colourless, odourless and tasteless, but its effects are potentially fatal. A generally accepted practice is to shut off the heating system if engine fumes (which may contain CO) are thought to be entering the cockpit. The danger arises if a crack or split is present in the exhaust system inside the heating shroud allowing carbon monoxide to enter the heating system.

The ventilation system consists of two cockpit vents, to the extreme right and left of the upper windscreen, which control fresh air from their respective external air intakes located in the inner wing leading edges. The cockpit vents are pulled out to allow fresh air to enter the cockpit, and can be rotated to direct the blast of air they provide. It is generally recommended that the vents be rotated to direct the air onto the inside of the windscreen, rather than directly into the face.

When the heating system is in use it is recommended that the fresh air vents be operated to give a comfortable temperature mix. Doing so will help to combat the possible danger of carbon monoxide poisoning, and on a more mundane level will stop the cabin becoming 'stuffy' and possibly inducing drowsiness in the pilot.

Seats and Harnesses

Up to 1972 models, only the seat backs are adjustable. From 1973 models the seats can be adjusted fore and aft in addition to the seat back adjustment. Fore and aft adjustment is made with a lever located under the front inboard edge of the seat cushion. When this lever is raised the seat can be slid forward or back along the seat tracks until the desired position is reached. The lever is pushed down and the seat should be locked in position. With the late (1976 model) 150s the seat height can also be adjusted.

The seat design of the 150 is subject to criticism in two areas. The first problem arises over the security of the mechanism that locks the seat on the seat rail in the desired fore/aft position (where the seats have fore and aft adjustment). The scenario is that when adjusted the seat fails to lock properly, undetected by the pilot. Then at some stage of flight (often just after take off) the seat runs rearward on the rails, taking the occupant with it. The possible consequences - especially if the pilot is flying solo and if the controls are not released as the seat slides back - can be imagined. Prevention being the best cure, it is essential to positively ensure that the seat is locked in position - not only after adjustment but also as part of the pre-take off checks. The problem is usually well known to those with some experience on these types, but 30' high just after take off is not a good place to find out for the first time.

A second problem concerns the seat backs. Fatigue cracking in the seat frames has been the cause of several seat collapses, with the same serious consequences as for the problems with the seat rails. In this instance the culprits are usually pilots who apply excessive force on the rudder pedals when applying the brakes, especially when setting the parking brake. By pressing hard against the seat back the frame is subject to undue forces leading to fatigue cracks; the problem of failing rudder pedals - caused in the same fashion - has already been covered.

Harness design may vary between different aircraft. As standard a lap strap will be fitted, with anchor points on the floor, together with a shoulder strap which anchors to the cabin roof. The shoulder strap may attach to the lap strap via a loop through which the lap strap is threaded. On later models a connecting link on the shoulder strap attaches to a clip on the the lap strap buckle. As an option inertia reel harnesses may be fitted, which integrate the lap and shoulder strap. Aerobats may be fitted with an aerobatic harness.

The use of the shoulder straps should be considered mandatory, as upper torso restraint has been shown to be a major factor in accident survivability. Final adjustment of the harness should be done when the seat is in the desired location.

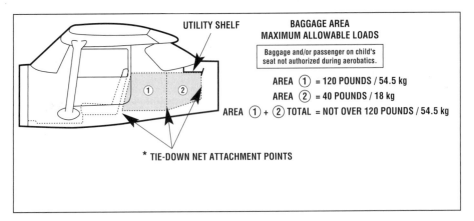

UTILITY SHELF

**BAGGAGE AREA
MAXIMUM ALLOWABLE LOADS**

Baggage and/or passenger on child's
seat not authorized during aerobatics.

AREA ① = 120 POUNDS / 54.5 kg
AREA ② = 40 POUNDS / 18 kg
AREA ① + ② TOTAL = NOT OVER 120 POUNDS / 54.5 kg

* TIE-DOWN NET ATTACHMENT POINTS

The baggage area behind the seats is sub divided into two sections. Maximum baggage to be carried in this area in total is 120 lbs (54 kg), with a maximum of 40 lbs (18 Kg) on the rear, sloping section of the compartment. Attention should be drawn to the weight and balance implications of weight in this area, it also must be remembered that for some manoeuvres the carriage of baggage is prohibited.

Doors And Windows

The 150 has a door each side of the cabin to allow for easy access. To close the door it is simply pulled shut using the arm rest. To check the door is closed before flight, pressure should be applied with the hand or elbow. To open the door the recessed door handle is pulled out at its forward edge - the door should open without any extra force being necessary. A door stop is fitted under each wing to prevent overstressing of the door hinges. Aerobats are fitted with 'quick release' doors. The door hinge pins are linked to a handle on the cockpit wall ahead of each door. In an emergency the door is unlatched, the release handle is pulled (withdrawing the hinge pins) and the door falls away.

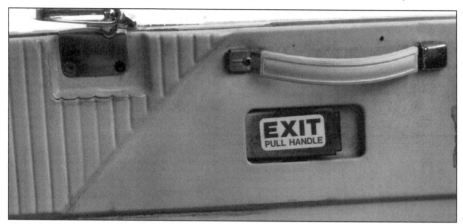

The simple door handle of the 150. Also visible is the window lever.

Although it is important for the doors to be properly latched for flight, the consequences of partial door opening in flight are usually not serious. If the aircraft is trimmed to approx. 65 knots it should be possible to slam the door shut. Where accidents do occur after a door opening in-flight, they are often caused by pilot distraction rather than as a direct result of the open door.

The window of either door can be opened in flight. The small lever at the centre base of the window is moved clockwise a quarter turn to the vertical, and the window opens outward. Each window has a spring-loaded retaining arm that helps to open the window and keep it in the open position. There will be some temporary fluctuations in the readings of the pressure instruments as the window is opened.

The quick release door hinges of the 150 Aerobat.

Visibility through the windows can be degraded by oil smears, bugs and other matter accumulating on the windows. For window cleaning a soft cloth and warm, soapy water are recommended. The use of petrol, alcohol, thinners and window cleaner sprays is not recommended. On the subject of visibility it is common practice on the 150, as with other high wing aircraft, to lift a wing slightly before a turn in that direction - ie lift the left wing a couple of degrees to check for traffic before turning to the left.

The Cessna 150

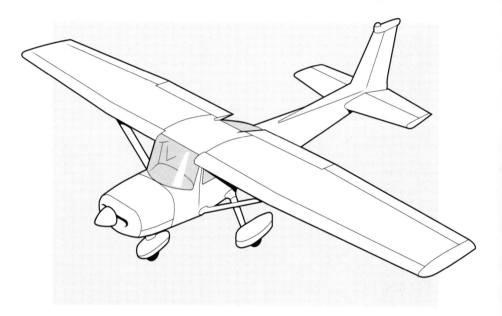

Limitations

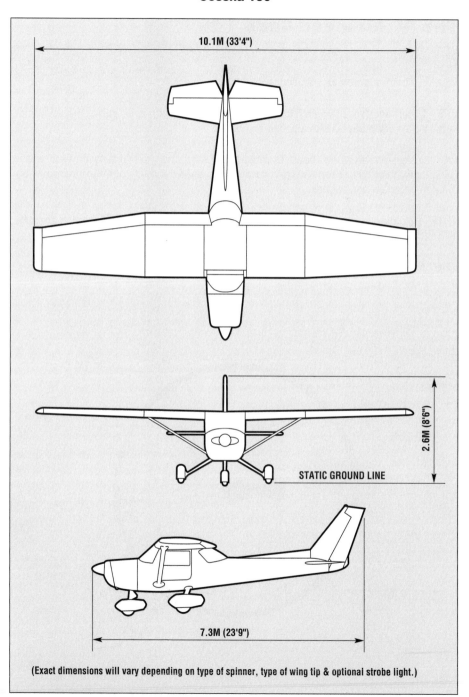

10.1M (33'4")

2.6M (8'6")

STATIC GROUND LINE

7.3M (23'9")

(Exact dimensions will vary depending on type of spinner, type of wing tip & optional strobe light.)

The 'V' Airspeed Code

VS0 - (Bottom of white arc) Stalling speed with full flap.

VS1 - (Bottom of green arc) Stalling speed 0 flap.

VFE - Maximum airspeed with flaps extended. Do not extend flaps above this speed, or fly faster than this speed with any flap extended.

VA - Design manoeuvring speed. Do not make full or abrupt control movements when flying faster than this speed. Design manoeuvring speed should not be exceeded when flying in turbulent conditions.

VNO - Maximum structural cruising speed. Do not exceed this speed except in smooth air conditions.

VNE - Never exceed speed. Do not exceed this airspeed under any circumstances.

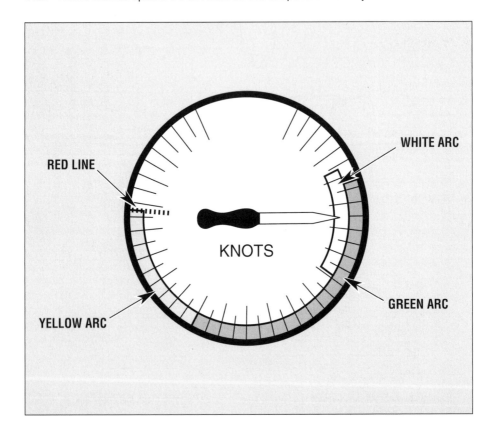

© Airplan Flight Equipment 1993

Cessna 150 Limitations

Airspeed Limitations - Cessna 150

(quoted speeds are CALIBRATED airspeed-CAS)

Note: C150 airspeed indicators are generally marked in MPH

	KNOTS	MPH	KPH
VNE	141	162	261
VNO	104	120	193
VA (at 1600 lbs)	95	109	176
VFE	87	100	161
Stalling Speed Clean	49	56	90
Stalling Speed Full Flap	43	49	79

Airspeed Indicator Markings (CAS)

RED LINE (Never exceed)	141	162	261
YELLOW ARC (Caution range)	104 - 141	120 - 162	193 - 261
GREEN ARC (Normal operating range)	49 - 104	56 - 120	90 - 193
WHITE ARC (Flap extended range)	43 - 87	49 - 100	79 - 161

Airspeed Limitations - Cessna 150M

(quoted speeds are INDICATED airspeed-IAS)

Note: C150 airspeed indicators are generally marked in MPH

	Knots	MPH	KPH
VNE	141	162	261
VNO	107	123	198
VA (at 1600 lbs)	97	112	180
VFE	85	98	158
Stalling Speed Clean	47	54	87
Stalling Speed Full Flap	42	49	77

Airspeed Indicator Markings (IAS)

RED LINE (Never Exceed)	141	162	261
YELLOW ARC (Caution range)	107 - 141	123 - 162	198 - 261
GREEN ARC (Normal operating range)	47 - 107	54 - 123	87 - 198
WHITE ARC (Flap extended range)	42 - 85	49 - 98	77 - 158

Maximum Demonstrated Crosswind Component Cessna F150M

Take Off 20 Knots
Landing 15 Knots

Airframe Limitations Cessna 150

WEIGHTS	lbs	Kg
Maximum Take Off Weight	1600	726
Maximum Landing Weight	1600	726
Maximum Baggage Weight	120	54

Note: the baggage compartment must be empty for aerobatic manoeuvres.

Performance Limitations

Service Ceiling - 12650 ft

Engine Limitations

	Tachometer	Instrument Marking
Maximum RPM	2750	Red Line
Normal Operating Range	2000 - 2750	Green Arc

	Oil Temperature	Instrument Marking
Normal Operating Range	up to 240°F	Green Arc
Maximum	240°F* (116°C)	Red Line

* 225°F some early aircraft

	Oil Pressure	Instrument Marking
Normal Operating Range	30 - 60 psi	Green Arc
Minimum	10 psi	Red Line
Maximum	100 psi	Red Line

Oil Quantity

	US quart	Litre
Note: dipstick is marked in US quarts		
Capacity	6	5.7
Minimum Safe Quantity	4	3.8

Fuel System

	US Gal	Imp Gal	Litre
Fuel Quantity - Standard Tanks			
Note: cockpit fuel gauges are marked in US gallons			
Total Capacity	26	21.6	98
Unusable Fuel	3.5	2.9	13
Usable Fuel (all flight conditions)	22.5	18.7	85

Miscellaneous Limitations

Nose Wheel Tyre Pressure	30 psi	2.10 bar
Main Wheel Tyre Pressure	21 psi	1.45 bar

Oil Grades

Engine oil is available in two types, straight mineral oil and ashless dispersant oil.

Straight mineral type - known mostly as straight oil - is usually only used when the engine is new, or after maintenance work on the engine. Straight oil grades are known by their number - ie 80, 100.

Ashless dispersant oils are more commonly used in service. These oil grades carry the prefix 'W', ie W80, W100. Ashless dispersant type - 'W' oil - must not be used where the engine is operating on straight oil, nor can 'W' oil be added to straight mineral oil. It is therefore very important to check which type of oil is currently being used in the engine and be sure only to add the same type.

Both types of oil are available in different grades, used according to the average ground air temperature. The recommended grades are set out as SAE numbers, but available in commercial grade numbers - which are different! The situation is more simple than it appears, to get the approximate commercial grade, double the SAE number, ie SAE 50 = commercial grade 100 (or W100). The table below shows the recommended grades for various surface temperature bands.

AVERAGE SURFACE AIR TEMPERATURE	Straight mineral type	COMMERCIAL GRADE
Above 40°F / 5°C	SAE 40	80
Below 40°F / 5°C	SAE 20 or SAE 10W30	55
AVERAGE SURFACE AIR TEMPERATURE	Ashless Dispersant type	COMMERCIAL GRADE
Above 40°F / 5°C	SAE 40	W80
Below 40°F / 5°C	SAE 10W30	

Fuel Grades

The Cessna 150 is certified for use with minimum grade fuel 80/87.

The table below shows the recommended fuel grades. It is wise to pay attention when your aircraft is being refuelled, especially if away from your usual airfield. More than one pilot has found out to their cost that piston engines designed for AVGAS do not run very well on AVTUR (Jet A-1). To help guard against this eventuality AVGAS fuelling points carry a RED sticker and AVTUR fuelling points a BLACK sticker. Most (but not all) 150s are also permitted to use Mogas (motor gasoline) ie. 4 Star petrol. Detailed operating procedures and restrictions are set out by the CAA in an Airworthiness Notice.

APPROVED FUEL GRADES

80/87

80

100LL

100L

100 * (formerly 100/130)

* grade 100 is acceptable for limited operation when grade 80 or 100LL is not available.

The Cessna 150

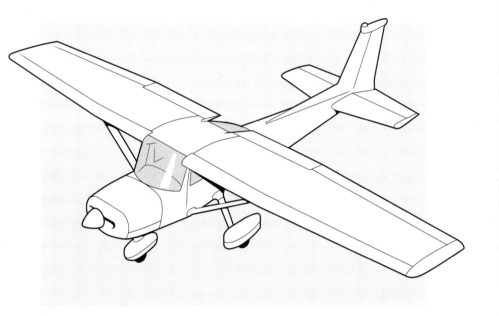

Handling The Cessna 150

Ground Handling

Whenever possible a towbar should be used for manually manoeuvring the aircraft. The towbar attaches to the nosewheel assembly and provides a point to push or pull as well as allowing accurate steering. When using a towbar take care not to exceed the nosewheel turning angle limit of 30°

Unfortunately a towbar is not always available when you need it. In this case the push/pulling points are the wing strut ends and undercarriage legs. Using the propeller to pull or push is very much a matter of personal choice - bearing in mind that it is virtually impossible to be sure that the propeller is not 'LIVE' - even with the keys out of the magneto switch. The leading edge of the tailplane MUST NOT be used as a pushing point - there are recorded cases of structural damage to the tailplane caused by incorrect ground handling. To steer the aircraft without a towbar, the tail must be lowered to raise the nosewheel clear of the ground, the aircraft can then be pivoted about the main wheels. The tail can be lowered by pushing down over the
tailplane front spar adjacent to the fuselage, or over a rear fuselage bulkhead. DO NOT push down on the outer tailplane or on the control surfaces. The aircraft flying instructor or operator should be able to point out the correct push down points.

Engine Starting

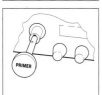

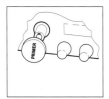

Starting the C150 is uncomplicated, but the ambient conditions and engine temperature are the principle factors to be considered. Somewhere between 2 and 6 primes are required for starting, generally the colder the ambient temperature and engine temperature, the more priming will be required. After priming the throttle is set to 1/4" open (that is 1/4" in); 'pumping' of the throttle - especially during starting - should be avoided as the accelerator pump in the carburettor can cause fuel to pool in the intake, leading to a fire risk.

Cranking of the starter should be limited to 12 seconds at a time due to the danger of the starter motor overheating. After a prolonged period of engine cranking without a successful start the starter should be allowed a few minutes to cool before a further starting attempt is made. The starter should not be operated after engine start as damage to the starter may result. The starter warning light should go out after engine start, if it remains lit the engine should be shut down without delay.

After start the oil pressure should register within 30 seconds, in exceptionally cold conditions 60 seconds may be required.

Should the oil pressure not register the engine should be shut down without delay. Readings on the suction gauge and ammeter are also checked after engine start.

Starting With a Suspected Flooded Engine

A flooded (over primed) engine is characterised by weak intermittent firing and puffs of black smoke during the attempted start. If it is suspected that the engine is flooded (over primed) the throttle should be opened fully and the mixture moved to idle cut off. If the engine starts the throttle should be retarded to the normal position and the mixture moved to fully rich.

Starting In Cold Ambient Conditions (below 0°c)

Starting will be more difficult in cold temperatures. The oil will be more viscous, the battery may lose up to half of its capacity and the fuel will not vapourise readily. A greater number of primes will be required, external power may be needed to supplement the aircraft battery and pre-heat may be necessary in very low temperatures.

Starting In Hot Ambient Conditions

There are few problems associated with engine starting in high temperatures. However one possibleproblem concerns fuel vapourisation after the engine has been running. After the engine is shut down the temperature of the various engine components will stabilise, some cooling, some heating. The fuel system tends to heat up and fuel in the lines may 'boil' or vapourise, this vapour will inhibit starting until the entire fuel system has filled with liquid fuel. This problem is generally at its worst between 30 and 60 minutes after engine shut down. The only real solution is to allow time for the fuel system to cool and to open the throttle slightly more than usual when starting.

Taxying

In the first few feet of taxying a brake check is normally carried out, followed by steering and differential brake checks in due course. To anyone used to aircraft with 'direct' steering rods from the rudder pedals to the nose wheel the spring link system of the 150 may at first seem very 'loose' and inexact. It should be remembered that the rudder pedals only steer the nosewheel through 10° either side of neutral, and differential braking is required to castor the nose wheel up to its limit of 30°. The 150 is easy to taxy, although practice may be needed in the increased use of the rudder pedals and differential braking when taxying in crosswind conditions. When taxying with a crosswind up to full rudder deflection may be required ie with a crosswind from the left, up to full right rudder may be required as the aircraft tries to 'weathercock' into wind.

The chart below shows recommended control column positions when taxying with the prevailing wind from the directions shown.

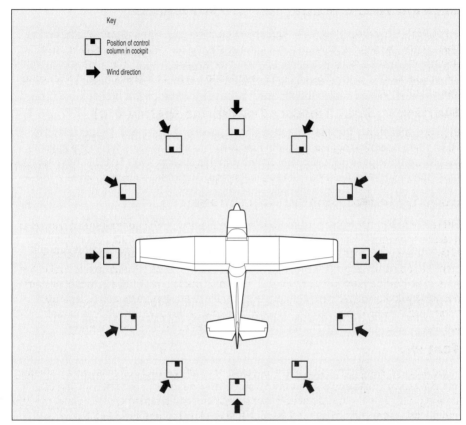

Speed control is important, especially when taxying over rough surfaces or in strong wind conditions. When slowing the aircraft the throttle should always be closed first, then the brakes evenly applied to slow the aircraft. If taxiing over loose stones or gravel the lowest possible RPM should be used to avoid damage to the propeller.

Power and Pre-Take-off Checks

The aircraft is usually positioned into wind to aid engine cooling and before beginning the power check the oil temperature should be in the green arc.

The engine is generally run up to 1700 RPM and the carburettor heat is checked. The subject of carb. icing is covered more fully later, however an important point to note is that the inlet for the 'hot' air is unfiltered, so dust, grass etc may well enter the engine when 'hot' air is selected, leading to increased engine wear. For this reason the use of carb. heat should be kept to the minimum necessary whilst on the ground.

The magnetos are checked individually, a small drop in RPM (no more than 150RPM) is the norm and shows that the ignition system is functioning properly. No drop at all in RPM when operating on one magneto may well indicate a malfunction in the ignition system, and the possibility of one or both magnetos staying 'live'. There should not be more than 75 RPM difference between magnetos. An excessive drop in RPM when operating on one magneto, especially when accompanied by rough running, may indicate fouled spark plugs or a faulty magneto. If fouled plugs are suspected it may be possible to clear the problem. The engine is advanced to about 2000 RPM with magnetos on 'BOTH' and the mixture leaned to give the 'peak' RPM. This should be held for about 10 seconds, then the mixture is returned to fully rich, power is brought back to 1700 RPM and the magnetos can be rechecked.

> **WARNING:** Excessive power setting and over lean mixture settings should be avoided during this procedure. If the problem does not clear the aircraft should be considered unserviceable.

The engine gauges are checked at 1700 RPM for normal indications, together with the suction gauge and ammeter.

During the pre-takeoff checks two items are of particular importance to the 150. The flap settings should always be visually checked. Problems with the flap operating system have led to instances of C 150s attempting take off with full flap, even though only 10° of flap was set, 10° of flap is the maximum permissible for take-off under any conditions. Attention should also be paid to the seat locking, due to the seat security problems already discussed.

Take-off

Normally take off is made with the mixture in the fully RICH position. At high elevation airfields (above say 3000' AMSL) it may be necessary to lean the mixture before take off to give full power.

For all take offs care must be taken to ensure that the feet remain clear of the toe brakes, this is best done by keeping the heels on the floor. Inadvertent pressure on the toe brakes can significantly slow the aircraft during the take off run and lead to directional control difficulties.

At the start of the take off run (as at all other times) the throttle should be opened smoothly and progressively. Rapid opening of the throttle should be specifically avoided, as it can lead to the accelerator pump 'flooding' the engine. The normal rotate speed is around 55 mph, with a climb speed of 70 - 80 mph dependent on conditions and operator procedures. The stated best rate-of-climb airspeed varies between models - from 73 mph to 78mph - check the individual aircraft flight manual. For 'short field' take offs the use of 10° of flap is common practice. Although the use of flap shortens the take off run, the benefit is lost in the climb out using the 'flaps up' best angle-of-climb airspeed. The best angle-of-climb airspeed varies between 64 mph to 70 mph depending on the exact model - again check the aircraft flight manual. Flap settings beyond 10° should not be used for take off as the increased lift is matched by a larger increase in drag and so is counterproductive.

On rough surfaces particularly it is important to protect the nose wheel by keeping weight off it during the take off run, although 'over-rotating' should be avoided as this will lengthen the take off run (and ruin the view ahead!).

Climbing

During climbing it is important to monitor the engine gauges, as the engine is operating at a high power setting but with a reduced cooling airflow compared to cruising flight. Lookout ahead is impaired by the high nose attitude and it is common practice to 'weave' the nose periodically during the climb to visually check the area ahead.

Cruising Flight

Cruising is normally done with a power setting of 65-75%. Typically a setting of 2350 RPM will give an indicated airspeed of around 100 mph. The flight manual states the recommended mixture leaning procedure to achieve the flight manual cruise performance, range and endurance.

If turbulent conditions are encountered in flight particular care must be taken to not exceed the Va (Design Manoeuvring Speed). Unfortunately differing models of 150 have differing Va airspeeds, ranging from 109 mph up to 122 mph - so it is essential to check the aircraft's flight manual for the exact figure.

Engine Handling

Engine rough running can be caused by a number of factors, it should be remembered that the majority of engine failures in light aircraft are caused by pilot error. After carburettor icing, fuel exhaustion (running out of fuel) features as a cause of engine failures on C150s.

Having sufficient fuel on board to complete the flight is a point of basic airmanship, mostly accomplished through proper flight planning and thorough pre-flight checks - especially a proper VISUAL check of the fuel contents.

Regular monitoring of the engine instruments may forewarn of an impending problem. HIGH OIL TEMPERATURE may indicate a faulty gauge, if not accompanied by a corresponding drop in oil pressure. As with most instances the action to be taken will depend on the pilot's judgment of the situation at the time. As general guidance a diversion to a suitable airfield, whilst remaining alert to the possibility of a sudden engine failure, would make a reasonable course of action. *Where high oil temperature is accompanied by low oil pressure engine failure may very well be imminent and the pilot should act accordingly*. High oil temperature might occur during a prolonged slow climb in hot conditions, in this instance increasing the airspeed to provide more cooling and reducing power if possible may restore oil temperature to normal. In the event of a LOW OIL PRESSURE reading, accompanied by a normal oil temperature reading, gauge failure may be the culprit and the pilot can consider actions similar to those for an oil temperature gauge failure. Where the low oil pressure is accompanied by a high oil temperature, engine failure could well be imminent and the pilot will want to act accordingly.

Stalling

Note: *The information in this section is no substitute for flying instruction under the guidance of a flying instructor familiar with the aircraft and its characteristics.*

The C 150 is conventional in its stalling behaviour. The stall warning horn activates 5 to 10 mph above the stall airspeed. The airspeed indicator is unreliable near to stall airspeeds and tends to under-read considerably. Due to 'position error' C-150 airspeed indicators tend to be marked in Calibrated Airspeed (CAS or RAS), which is Indicated Airspeed (IAS) corrected for position error. Approaching stall airspeeds the airspeed indicator needle may well be almost 'off-the-clock', even though the aircraft is still flying at over 40 mph. The use of power will lower the stalling speed, whilst turning flight raises the stalling speed. With the flaps down some elevator buffeting occurs prior to the stall. The use of flaps, power or turning flight considerably increases the chances of a wing drop at the stall. When practising stalls the possibility of a wing drop can be reduced by keeping the aircraft in balance during the approach to the stall. Typical height loss for a full stall with a conventional recovery (using power) is about 100'.

Spins

Note: *The information in this section is no substitute for flying instruction under the guidance of a flying instructor familiar with the aircraft and its characteristics.*

Cessna have produced a detailed supplement covering the spinning characteristics and recommended recovery action for the single engined Cessna aircraft. It is highly recommended that you read this supplement BEFORE intentional spinning.

The Cessna 150 is approved for intentional spinning, however -

INTENTIONAL SPINS WITH FLAPS EXTENDED ARE PROHIBITED.

As with stalling several factors can affect the behaviour of the aircraft in the spin. It is quite possible to devote a whole book just to this subject and it is not the intention here to write a text book on spinning. However some points are worthy of mention. The weight of the aircraft (and particularly the cg position) has a noticeable effect on the spin, a forward cg position makes a pure spin more difficult to obtain, a spiral with increasing airspeed and 'g' loads is more likely. With aft c.g. positions the spin is easier to achieve, and recoveries may take longer. High weights tend to extend the spin recovery due to the increase in inertia. The use of power in the spin tends to lead to a 'flatter' spin attitude and recoveries may be lengthened. Finally the position of the ailerons is important in spinning. The ailerons should be held NEUTRAL throughout the spin and recovery.

Following the spin entry the aircraft enters a stage lasting about two turns where the rate of rotation increases with a nose down attitude of 60° - 70°. After about two turns the nose attitude rises to about 45° nose down and the aircraft enters the steady spin. It must be emphasised that this very general description is dependent on many factors as already discussed. At forward cg positions the steady phase of the spin may not occur and spiral tendencies may become apparent instead. The 150M model aircraft may not exhibit the change to the steady phase and these models tend to have slightly quicker recoveries.

Recovery from the spin can be summarised as follows:

● Check ailerons neutral and throttle closed.

● Apply and hold full opposite rudder (opposite to the direction of spin).

● Just after the rudder reaches the stop move the control wheel forward until the stall is broken and the spin stops.

● When rotation stops centralise the rudder and recover from the ensuing dive.

In the early stages of the spin (first two turns approx.) recovery can be almost instantaneous, especially at forward cg positions. Once in the steady spin, recovery is more likely to take up to 1 turn. In all spinning it is important to ensure that the proper recovery actions are taken and that the recovery control positions are held until recovery occurs.

Descent

The descent may be powered or glide, for the glide a speed of around 70mph is standard. Again the exact best glide airspeed varies between models from 65 mph to 70 mph - check the aircraft's flight manual. Where flaps are used the rate of descent increases markedly. The initial lowering of flap leads to a distinct nose up pitching and reduced airspeed. Especially at airspeeds close to VFE the trim change can be quite marked and the aircraft may 'balloon' whilst the attitude is changed and the aircraft re-trimmed. Cessna do not recommend side slipping with flaps extended beyond 20° due to aerodynamic buffeting of the tail surfaces. Most operators discourage sideslipping with any flap extended. Apart from other considerations the 150 can take on a high rate of descent in a glide with flaps extended, the additional descent rate caused by sideslipping can prove excessive when close to the ground.

The low power settings usually used during the descent and a possible prolonged descent into warmer air, provide ideal conditions for carburettor icing. Full carburettor heat should be used where necessary. In a glide descent power should be added for short periods throughout the descent to help prevent spark plug fouling, rapid cylinder cooling and of course carb. icing.

Landing

The Cessna 150 is almost universally described as being an easy aircraft to land. This does not prevent the Cessna 150 (as with many other light aircraft) appearing year after year in landing accident reports. It is rare that anybody is hurt in these accidents, but the reports seem surprisingly similar:

"Cessna FRA.150M ——-. Nose landing gear collapsed following third bounce on landing at ——-."

"Cessna F.150M ——. Nose undercarriage collapsed as a result of a heavy landing at ————."

"Cessna FA 150K ——-. Nosewheel broke off following a bounce on landing at ———-."

As already covered the nosewheel is nowhere near as strong as the main undercarriage, but there is no need for its strength to be tested if a proper approach and landing technique is used. Normal approach speed for an approach with flap is about 70mph, usually a little higher for a flapless approach. Short field approaches are made with full flap and a recommended speed of 58 - 60 mph dependent on aircraft model. Incorrect approach speed is a primary cause of 'ballooning', which often leads to bouncing. Bouncing also arises where the aircraft is allowed to touch down at too high a speed, usually in a level attitude rather than a nose up attitude. The correct action in either a 'balloon' or a bounce is to GO AROUND without delay.

The correct landing technique is to approach at the proper speed, 'flare' or 'hold off', close the throttle and gradually raise the nose to ensure a low touch down speed on the MAINWHEELS FIRST, with the nose wheel still off the ground. As the aircraft slows down correct use of the elevators means the nose wheel is allowed to gently contact the surface some time after the initial mainwheel contact. Again there is no substitute for flying instruction in the proper technique with a flying instructor.

The correct landing attitude may be more difficult to achieve when full flap is extended, as the aircraft will tend to land 'flat'. During a glide approach with full flap the high rate of descent and large change in attitude required to flare takes some getting used to. Most operators do not recommend the use of full flap in normal circumstances, not least because of the amount of skill required for a safe full flap go around.

The go around with full flap in the 150 poses two main problems. Firstly when full power is applied there is a considerable trim change, some pilots may have difficulty in holding the attitude required until able to use the trim to reduce the control force. Secondly the flaps will need to be raised quickly to 20°, so that a reasonable rate of climb can be established. The 150 does not have a good climb performance with full flap extended, it is not un-common to find that the aircraft simply will not climb with 40° of flap extended. The flap system of the 150 is designed to move the flaps more quickly over the range between 40°-20° than between 20°-0°, typically raising flaps from 40° to 20° takes 2-3 seconds.

Parking and Tie Down

The aircraft is generally parked into wind, it is good practice to stop with the nosewheel straight so that the rudder is not deflected. All switches should be off, the doors closed and the control lock fitted. In extremely cold weather it may be advisable NOT to set the parking brake as moisture may freeze the brakes, also the parking brake should not be set if there is reason to believe that the brakes are overheated. If for any reason the parking brake is not set the wheels should be 'chocked'.

When strong winds are forecast, all possible precautions should be taken.

When tying down the aircraft the following technique is recommended:

- Park aircraft into wind with the control wheel lock in.

- Ropes, cables or chains are attached to the wing tie down points and secured to ground anchor points.

- If desired a rope (not cable or chain) can be secured to the exposed portion of the engine mount and secured to a ground anchor point.

- A rope can be passed through the tail tie down point and each end secured at a 45° angle either side of the tail.

- External control locks (particularly to the rudder) may be advisable in strong or gusty wind conditions.

It is also prudent to use a pitot cover, particularly if the aircraft will be left unattended for some time.

The Cessna 150

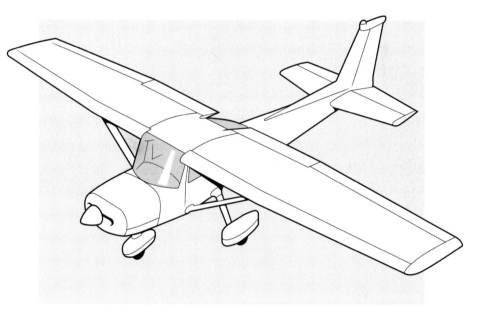

MIXTURE AND CARB. ICING SUPPLEMENT.

Carburettor Icing

Almost certainly the most common cause of engine rough running, and complete engine failures, is carburettor icing. Despite this carburettor icing remains a widely misunderstood subject, with many pilots' knowledge of the subject being limited to a feeling that the carb heat should be used regularly in flight, without really knowing the symptoms of carb. icing or the conditions most likely to cause its formation.

How Carburettor Icing Forms

IMPACT ICING occurs when ice forms over the external air inlet (air filter) and inside the induction system leading to the carburettor. This type of icing occurs with the temperature below 0°C whilst flying in cloud, or in precipitation (ie rain, sleet or snow). These conditions are also conducive to airframe icing, and this aircraft is NOT CLEARED FOR FLIGHT INTO KNOWN ICING CONDITIONS, which clearly these are. So, assuming the aircraft is operated legally within its limitations, this form of icing should not occur, and is not considered further.

CARBURETTOR ICING is caused by a temperature drop inside the carburettor, which can happen even in conditions where other forms of icing will not occur. The causes of this temperature drop are twofold:

1. Fuel Icing - the evaporation of fuel inside the carburettor. Liquid fuel changes to fuel vapour and mixes with the induction air causing a large temperature drop. If the temperature inside the carburettor falls below 0°C, water vapour in the atmosphere condenses into ice, usually on the walls of the carburettor passage adjacent to the fuel jet, and on the throttle valve. Generally fuel icing is responsible for around 70% of the temperature drop in the carburettor.

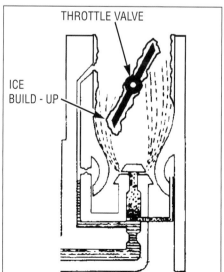

THROTTLE VALVE

ICE BUILD - UP

2. Throttle icing - the temperature loss caused by the acceleration of air and consequent pressure drop around the throttle valve. This effect may again take the temperature below 0°C, and water vapour in the inlet air will condense into ice on the throttle valve. This practical effect is a demonstration of Bernoulli's Principle.

As fuel and throttle icing generally occur together, they are considered just as carburettor icing.

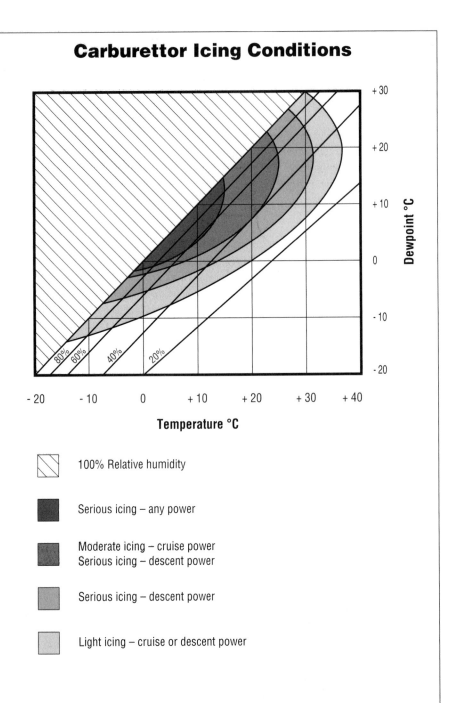

Carburettor Icing Conditions

100% Relative humidity

Serious icing – any power

Moderate icing – cruise power
Serious icing – descent power

Serious icing – descent power

Light icing – cruise or descent power

Conditions Likely To Lead To Carburettor Icing

Two criteria govern the likelihood of carburettor icing conditions, the AIR TEMPERATURE and the RELATIVE HUMIDITY.

The ambient air temperature is important, BUT NOT BECAUSE THE TEMPERATURE NEEDS TO BE BELOW 0°C, OR EVEN CLOSE TO FREEZING. The temperature drop in the carburettor can be up to 30°C, so carburettor icing can (and does) occur in hot ambient conditions. No wonder carburettor icing is sometimes referred to as refrigeration icing. Carburettor icing is considered a possibility within the temperature range of -10°C to +30°C.

The relative humidity (a measure of the water content of the atmosphere) is the major factor. The greater the water content in the atmosphere (the higher the relative humidity), the greater the risk of carburettor icing. That said the relative humidity (RH) does not to have to be 100% (ie visible water droplets - cloud, rain), for carburettor icing to occur. Carburettor icing is considered a possibility at relative humidity values as low as 30%, but it is rare that the RH gets this low in Europe. Herein lies the real danger of carburettor icing, that it can occur in such a wide range of conditions. Obviously the pilot must be alert to the possibility of carburettor icing at just about all times. Flight in or near cloud, or in other visible moisture (ie rain) might be an obvious cause of carburettor icing, but - VISIBLE MOISTURE DOES NOT NEED TO BE PRESENT FOR CARBURETTOR ICING TO OCCUR.

Symptoms Of Carburettor Icing

In this aircraft, fitted with a fixed pitch propeller, the symptoms of carburettor icing are straightforward. A loss of RPM will be the first symptom, although this is often first noticed as a loss of altitude. As the icing becomes more serious, engine rough running may occur.

Carburettor icing is often detected during the use of the carburettor heat. Normally when the carburettor heat is used, a small drop in rpm occurs, when the control is returned to cold (off) the rpm restores to the same as before the use of carburettor heat. If the rpm restores to a higher figure than before the carburettor heat was used, it can be reasonably supposed that some form of carburettor icing was present.

Use Of Carburettor Heat

Apart from the normal check of carburettor heat during the power checks, it may be necessary to use the carburettor heat on the ground if carburettor icing is suspected. Safety considerations apart, the use of carburettor heat on the ground should be kept to a minimum, as the hot air inlet is unfiltered, and so sand or dust can enter the engine, increasing engine wear.

Carburettor icing is generally considered to be very unlikely with the engine operating at above 75% power, ie during the take-off and climb. Carburettor heat should not be used with the engine operating at above 75% power (ie full throttle) as detonation may occur. Detonation is the uncontrolled burning of fuel in the cylinders, literally an explosion, and will cause serious damage to the engine very quickly. Apart from the danger of detonation, the use of carburettor heat reduces the power the engine produces. In any situation where full power is required (ie take-off, climb, go-around) the carburettor heat must be off (cold).

Very few operators recommend the use of anything other than FULL carburettor heat. A normal carburettor icing check will involve leaving the carburettor heat on (hot) for 5-10 seconds, although the pilot may wish to vary this dependent on the conditions. The use of carburettor heat does increase the fuel consumption, and this may be a factor to consider if the aircraft is being flown towards the limit of its range/endurance in possible carburettor icing conditions.

With carburettor icing present, the use of carburettor heat may lead to a large drop in rpm, with rough running. The instinctive reaction is to put the carburettor heat back to cold (off), and quickly. This is, however, the wrong action. Chances are this rough running is a good thing, and the carburettor heat should be left on (hot) until the rough running clears and the rpm rises. In this instance the use of carburettor heat has melted a large amount of accumulated icing and the melted ice is passing through the engine, causing temporary rough running.

Care should be taken when flying in very cold ambient conditions (below -10°C). In these conditions the use of carburettor heat may actually raise the temperature in the carburettor to that most conducive to carburettor icing. Generally when the temperature

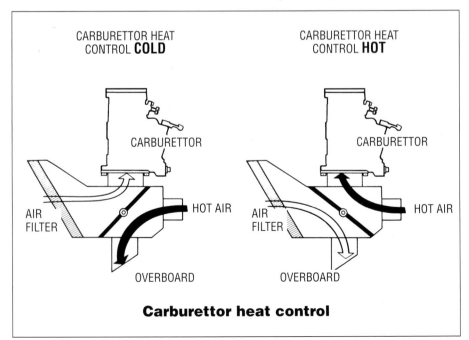

Carburettor heat control

in the carburettor is below -8°C moisture forms directly into ice crystals which pass through the engine.

The rpm loss normally associated with the use of carburettor heat is caused by the reduced density of the hot air entering the carburettor, leading to an over rich mixture entering the engine. If the carburettor heat has to be left constantly on (hot) - ie flight in heavy rain and cloud - it may be advisable to lean the mixture in order to maintain rpm and smooth engine running.

It is during the descent (and particularly the glide descent) that carburettor icing is most likely to occur. The position of the throttle valve (ie almost closed) is a contributory factor, and even though the carburettor heat is normally applied throughout a glide descent, the low engine power will reduce the temperature of the hot air selected with the carburettor heat control. In addition a loss of power may not be readily noticed. The propeller is likely to windmill even after a complete loss of power and so a full loss of power may only be apparent when the throttle is opened at the bottom of the descent. This is one good reason for opening the throttle to 'warm the engine' at intervals during a glide descent.

The Mixture Control

The aircraft is provided with a mixture control so that the pilot can adjust the fuel/air mixture entering the engine. The cockpit mixture control operates a needle valve between the float bowl and the main metering jet. This valve controls the fuel flow to the main metering jet to adjust the mixture, with the mixture control in the ICO position (fully lean) the valve is fully closed.

Reasons For Adjusting The Mixture

Correct leaning of the engine mixture will enable the engine to be operated at its most efficient in terms of fuel consumption. With the increased use of 100LL fuel, leaning is also important to reduce spark plug fouling.

The most efficient engine operation is obtained with a fuel/air ratio of about 1:15, that is 1 part fuel to 15 parts air. In fact with the mixture set to fully rich, the system is designed to give a slightly richer mixture than ideal, typically about 1:12. This slightly over rich mixture reduces the possibility of pre-ignition or detonation, and aids cylinder cooling.

As altitude increases the air density decreases. Above about 3000' the reduced air density can lead to an over rich mixture. If the mixture becomes excessively rich, power will be lost, rough running may be evident and ultimately engine failure will occur due to a 'rich cut'. It is for this reason that the mixture control is provided to ensure the correct fuel/air ratio, typically it is used when cruising above 3000'.

The flight manuals for some older aircraft recommend leaning only above 5000'. However with the increasing use of AVGAS 100LL, and the plug fouling problems sometimes associated with 100LL, most operators recommend leaning once above 3000'.

Effect of Mixture Adjustment

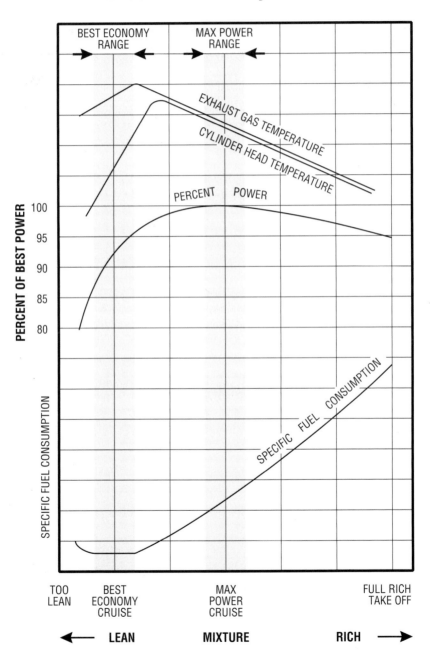

© Airplan Flight Equipment 1993

Use Of The Mixture Control

For take-off and climb the mixture should be fully rich, the only exception being operation from a high density altitude airport when leaning may be necessary to ensure the availability of max. power. On reaching a cruising altitude above about 3000' the cruise power should be set, and then leaning can be carried out (note: generally leaning with over 75% power set is not recommended). If climbing above about 5000', full throttle will be less than 75% power on a normally aspirated engine and so leaning may be permissible to maintain smooth running.

Assuming that there is no Exhaust Gas Temperature (EGT) gauge and no cylinder head temperature gauge, the primary instrument to watch when leaning is the RPM gauge (tachometer).

To lean the engine, the recommended power setting (RPM) is set with the throttle. Next, with a constant throttle setting, the mixture control is slowly moved back (leaned). If leaning is required the RPM will increase slowly, peak, and then decrease as the mixture is leaned, if leaning is continued the engine will ultimately run rough and lose power.

If the mixture is set to achieve peak RPM, the maximum power mixture has been achieved.

If the mixture is set to give a tachometer reading 25 - 50 rpm less than peak rpm on the 'lean' side, the best economy mixture has been achieved. This setting is the one that many aircraft manufacturers recommend (25-50 RPM on the 'lean side' of peak RPM), and their performance claims are based on such a procedure.

Using a mixture that is too lean is a false economy, and will lead to serious engine damage sooner or later. Detonation (an uncontrolled explosive combustion of the mixture in the cylinder) is particularly dangerous, and can lead to an engine failure in a very short time. The use of a fully rich mixture during full power operations is specifically to ensure engine cooling and guard against detonation.

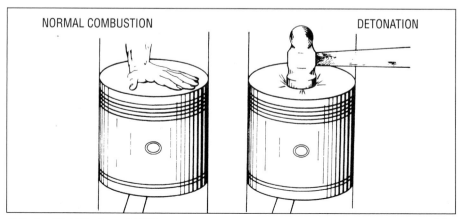

NORMAL COMBUSTION   DETONATION

For any change in operating conditions (altitude, power setting) the mixture will need to be reset. It is particularly important that the mixture is set to fully rich before increasing the power setting.

During a descent from a high altitude, the mixture will gradually become too lean if not reset, leading to excessive cylinder temperatures, power loss and ultimately engine failure. Normally the mixture is set to fully rich prior to landing, unless operating at a high elevation airfield.

Moving the mixture to the fully lean position - ICO (Idle Cut Off) - closes the needle valve and so stops fuel supply to the main metering jet. This is the normal method for closing down the engine and ensures that no unburnt mixture is left in the engine.

The Cessna 150

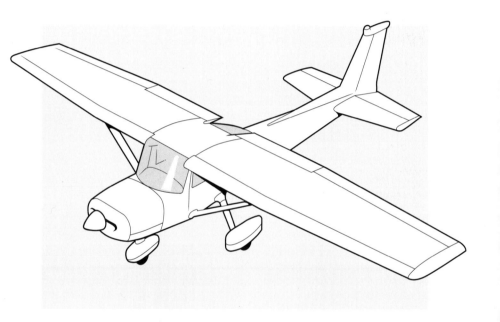

Expanded C150 Pre Flight Checklist

Approaching Aircraft

Check for and remove any tie downs, external control locks, pitot cover and wheel chocks.

Look for any oil & fuel spillages from aircraft.

Remove any ice & frost from ALL surfaces.

Check for access to taxiways, obstructions, loose gravel etc.

Look to see if aircraft is on a level surface. Sloping ground will affect the visual check of fuel contents.

In Cabin

1. **Internal Control Locks & Covers** .... Remove and stow securely

2. **Magneto Switches** .... Check OFF and key out

3. **Parking Brake** .... Ensure parking brake is set by pushing on strut

4. **Control Wheel Lock** .... Remove and stow

5. **Master Switch** .... On

   Turn on Pitot heater, anti-collision beacon, landing lights and navigation lights. Leave cockpit and check in turn :

6. **Pitot Heat** .... Check with fingers that pitot head is warm (it may take a minute or so to warm up)

7. **Anti-Collision Beacon** .... Check operation of rotating tail light

8. **Landing/Nav lights** .... Check.
   For Navigation lights colours are :
   PORT(Left) - RED; STARBOARD(Right) - GREEN; REAR(Tail) - WHITE

   Return to cockpit and turn off electrical services as in above

9. **Fuel Cock** .... Check on - check contents gauges

10. **Flaps** .... Check flap area clear. Lower fully (40°).

11. **Master Switch** .... Off

12. **Trimmer** .... Check position neutral using cockpit indicator

13. **First Aid Kit** .... In position, secure

14. **Fire Extinguisher** .... In position, secure & serviceable (gauge at top should be in green arc)

   Leave cockpit, watch your head on the lowered flaps!

External

Begin under wing. This should also be where you complete your checks.

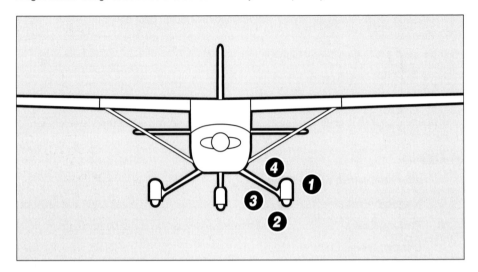

Port Undercarriage

1. **Tyre** .... Check for tread & general condition.
   Check for correct inflation. Check alignment of creep marks.

2. **Hydraulic Lines** .... Check for leaks (Red fluid).

3. **Disc Brake** .... Should be shiny, not rusty or pitted.

4. **Leg & Fairing** .... Check condition esp. GRP fairing.
   Look for mud or stone damage on wing & flap surface above and behind
   undercarriage.

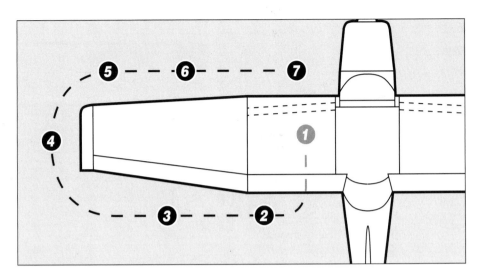

Port Wing

1 **Strut** .... Check condition and security of strut and fairing.

2. **Flap** .... Upper and lower surface condition. Particularly check inner lower surface for mud or stone damage from wheels. Check linkages and runners secure and greased.

3. **Aileron** .... Upper and lower surface condition, linkages & hinges secure, balance weight (lower inside edge) secure (with fingers inside hinge line hold the aileron still with other hand). Check full and free movement - DO NOT USE FORCE.

4. **Wing Tip** .... Condition, security. Navigation lights unbroken. (This area is particularly vulnerable to hangar damage)

5. **Lower Wing Surface** .... Check surface condition.

6. **Wing Leading Edge** .... Check for dents along entire length Check stall warner. Check pitot head perforations unblocked - DO NOT BLOW INTO PITOT. Check fuel tank vent unblocked.

7. **Fuel Tank** .... CHECK CONTENTS VISUALLY. Resecure cap. Whilst at fuel cap check upper wing surface condition. Take fuel drain sample from under wing if necessary - check for correct colour, water bubbles or sediment. Check drain not leaking.

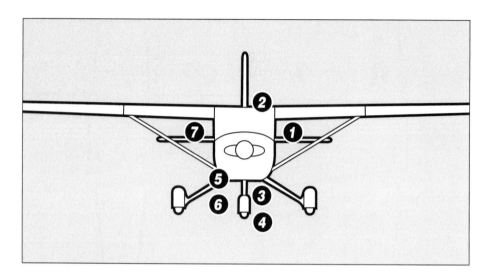

Front Fuselage & Engine

1. **Port Cowling** .... Check general condition and security. Check static vent clear - DO NOT BLOW INTO VENT.

2. **Windscreen** .... Should be clean and insect free.

3. **Nose Leg** .... Oleo extension. Linkages, nuts & split pins secure. No leakage from shimmy damper or oleo.

4. **Nose Wheel** .... Check for tread & general condition. Check for correct inflation. Check alignment of creep marks.

5. **Front Cowling** .... Check condition & security. Intakes clear, Landing lights unbroken.

6. **Propeller** .... Look for cracks or chips especially leading edge. Check spinner secure and condition good. DO NOT MOVE OR SWING PROPELLER.

7. **Starboard Cowling** .... Open access flap, check oil level. DO NOT overtighten dipstick on resecuring. Operate fuel strainer, if applicable, into a fuel sampler. Check fuel strainer closed and not leaking. Check access flap properly closed, cowling secure and in good condition.

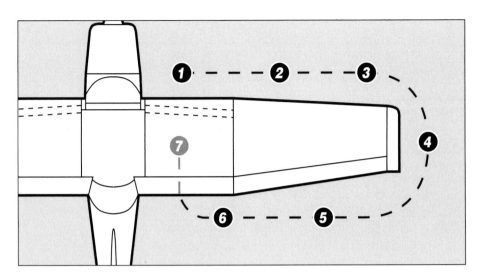

Starboard Wing

1. **Fuel Tank** .... CHECK CONTENTS VISUALLY. Resecure cap. Whilst at fuel cap check wing upper surface. Take fuel drain sample from under wing if necessary. Check drain not leaking.

2. **Wing Leading Edge** .... Check for dents along entire length.

3. **Lower Wing Surface** .... Check surface condition.

4. **Wing Tip** .... Condition, security. Navigation lights unbroken.

5. **Aileron** .... Upper and lower surface condition, linkages & hinges secure, balance weight (lower inside edge) secure. Remember to watch for aileron movement whilst checking inside hinge line. Check full and free movement gently - DO NOT USE FORCE.

6. **Flap** .... Upper and lower surface condition especially above and behind undercarriage. Check linkages and runners secure and greased.

7. **Strut** .... Condition and security of strut and fairings.

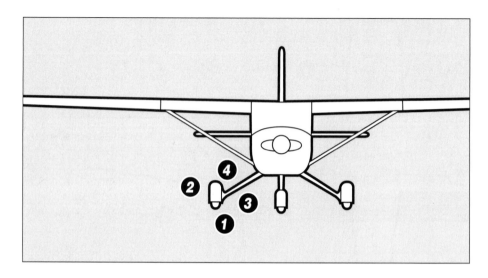

Starboard Undercarriage

1. **Tyre** .... Check for tread & general condition. Check for correct inflation. Check alignment of creep marks.

2. **Hydraulic Lines** .... Check for leaks (Red fluid).

3. **Disc Brake** .... Should be shiny, not rusty or pitted.

4. **Leg & Fairing** .... Check condition esp. GRP fairing. Look for mud or stone damage on wing & flap surface near undercarriage.

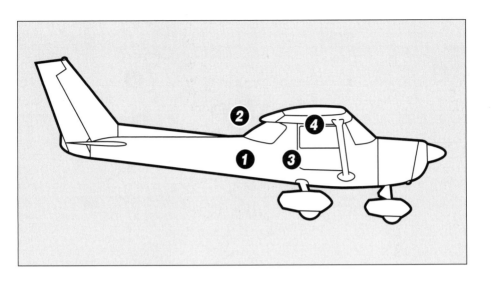

Starboard Fuselage

1. **Skin** .... General surface condition upper and lower, look for wrinkles, dents or punctures.

2. **Radio Aerials** .... Check secure.

3. **Cockpit Door** .... Latches and hinges secure.

4. **Windows** .... Check clean.

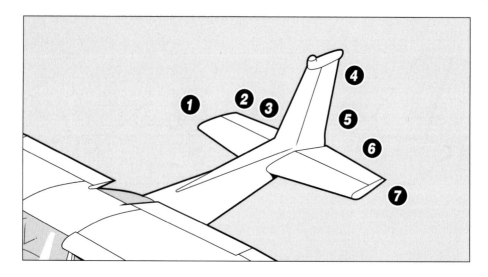

Tail Unit

1   **Starboard Tailplane** .... Check upper and lower surface condition, check security.

2   **Starboard Elevator** .... Check upper and lower surface condition. Check linkages, gently check full and free movement. DO NOT USE FORCE.

3   **Trim Tab** .... Check condition, linkages and correct movement in relation to elevator.

4   **Tail Fin** .... Check condition, also fairings, aerials and rotating beacon.

5   **Rudder** .... Check condition, navigation light, nuts and split pins. Full and free movement - DO NOT USE FORCE. Check tail tie down point.

6   **Port Elevator** .... Check condition, check linkages, gently check full and free movement - DO NOT USE FORCE.

7   **Port Tailplane** .... Check condition and security.

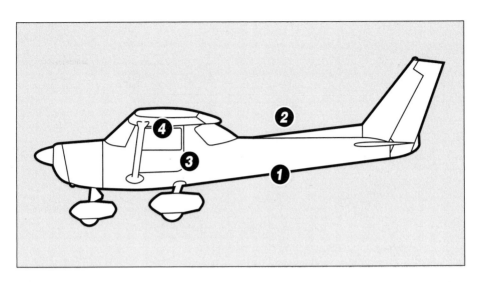

Port Fuselage

1. **Skin** .... General surface condition, upper and lower, look for any wrinkles, dents or punctures.

2. **Radio Aerials** .... Check secure.

3. **Cockpit door** .... Check latches & hinges.

4. **Windows** .... Check clean.

IMPORTANT

REMEMBER: FULL REFERENCE MUST BE MADE TO AIRCRAFT FLIGHT MANUAL, PILOTS OPERATING HANDBOOK, AIPs, FLYING SCHOOL SYLLABUS/PILOTS ORDER BOOK, ETC

IF IN DOUBT - ASK

The Cessna 150

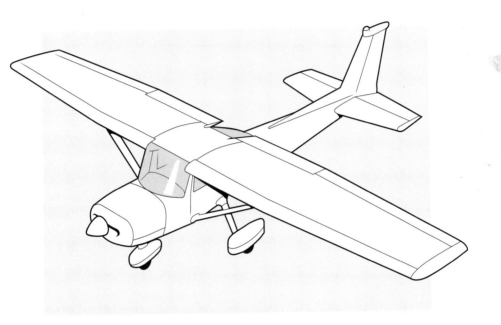

C150 Loading and Performance

Loading

Aircraft loading can divided into two areas, the aircraft weight and the centre of gravity (cg) position.

The aircraft must be loaded so that its weight is below the certified maximum take off weight - 1600 lbs/726Kg. The weight limit is set primarily as a function of the lifting capability of the aircraft, which is largely determined by the wing design and engine power of the aircraft. Operating the aircraft when it is over weight will adversely effect the aircraft handling and performance, such as:

Increased take off speed and slower acceleration

Increased runway length required for take off

Reduced rate of climb

Reduced maximum altitude capability

Reduced range and endurance

Reduction in manoeuvrability and controllability

Increased stall speed

Increased approach and landing speed

Increased runway length required for landing

The aircraft must also be loaded to ensure that its centre of gravity (cg) is within set limits, normally defined as a forward and aft limit aft of the datum, for this aircraft the datum is the lower forward face of the firewall. The forward limit is determined by the amount of elevator control available at landing speed, the aft limit is determined by the stability and controllability of the aircraft whilst manoeuvring. Attempted flight with the cg position outside the set limits (either forward or aft) will lead to control difficulties and quite possibly loss of control of the aircraft.

When loading the aircraft it is standard practice to calculate the weight and c.g. position of the aircraft at the same time, commonly known as the weight and balance calculation. Before going further it must be emphasised that the following examples are provided for illustrative purposes only. Each INDIVIDUAL aircraft has an INDIVIDUAL weight schedule that is valid only for that aircraft, and is dependent amongst other things on the equipment fitted to the aircraft. If the aircraft has any major modification, repair or new equipment fitted a new weight schedule will be produced. Therefore for any loading or performance calculations you must use the documents for the specific aircraft you will be using.

As well as setting out limits the aircraft documents will also give lever arms for each item of loading. The lever arm is a distance from the aircraft datum to the item.

The weight multiplied by its lever arm gives its moment. Thus a set weight will have a greater moment the further away from the datum it is.

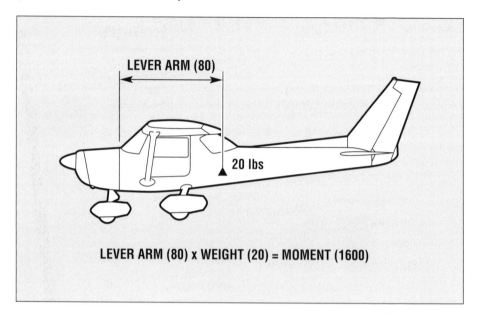

LEVER ARM (80) x WEIGHT (20) = MOMENT (1600)

The operating weight of the aircraft can be split into three categories:

STANDARD (EMPTY) WEIGHT - the weight of the aircraft, including unusable fuel (and normally full oil). The weight and cg position of the aircraft in this condition will be noted in the weight schedule.

VARIABLE LOAD - weight of the crew (ie pilot). The certified minimum crew for this aircraft is one pilot (!). The weight schedule will give the lever arm for this load.

DISPOSABLE LOAD - weight of a passenger, fuel and baggage. Again the weight schedule will give a lever arm for each of these loads.

Firstly the pilot will need to calculate a weight for the variable and disposable load. It is obviously important to work in one set of units (either lbs or kgs). This becomes more complicated for the fuel load where volume (litres, imperial gallons or US gallons) will need to be converted into weight. This may be done in the weight schedule, but conversion tables are set out in section 7.

Weight And Centre Of Gravity Schedule

PRODUCED BY :

GROSVENOR AVIATION SERVICES (ENGINEERING) LIMITED

AIRCRAFT TYPE: **PIPER PA38-112**

NATIONALITY AND REGISTRATION MARKS: **G-BGRR**

CONSTRUCTOR'S SERIAL No: **78A0336**

MAXIMUM PERMISSIBLE WEIGHT: **1670 lbs**

MAXIMUM LANDING WEIGHT: **1670 lbs**

CENTRE OF GRAVITY LIMITS: **REFER TO FLIGHT MANUAL REP No. FAA 2126**

ALL LEVER ARMS ARE DISTANCES IN INCHES EITHER FORE OR AFT OF DATUM.

PART 'A' BASIC WEIGHT

The basic weight of this aircraft as calculated from Planeweighs Limited Report No.1034 weighed on 08.07.88. at Manchester Airport is: **1182 lbs**

The centre of gravity of aircraft in the same condition (aft of the datum) is: **74.66 ins**.

The total Moment about the datum in this condition in lb ins. is: **88254.45**

The DATUM referred to is defined in the Flight Manual, which is **66.25 ins**. forward of Wing leading edge.

The basic weight includes the weight of 12 lbs unusable fuel and 45 lbs of oil and the weight of items indicated in Appendix 1 which comprises the list of basic equipment carried.

SAMPLE ONLY

Each individual aircraft has an individual weight schedule, valid only for that aircraft. The weight schedule will state lever arms for each item of loading.

Mathematical Weight and Balance Calculation

Using this method of calculation all the item weights are listed, along with their respective lever arms.

Firstly all the weights are totalled - to check that the weight is below the maximum permitted. Assuming this is the case, the balance is then calculated. Each item weight is multiplied by the respective lever arm to give the moment (except the basic weight, where this calculation has already been done in the weight schedule). Normally the lever arm is aft of the datum, and so is a positive figure. If the lever arm is forward of the datum, the lever arm and resulting moment are negative - although obviously the weight of the item is NOT deducted from the total weight. All the moments are added together to give the total moment. Dividing the total moment by the total weight gives the centre of gravity position. This can be checked against the limits set out in the weight schedule and flight manual.

Rather than using a centre of gravity position envelope graph, C-150 flight manuals tend to have a graph where the total weight is plotted against total moment - as will be seen later.

The following calculation is done in lbs and inches, however check carefully which units are being used for the aircraft you are flying - French built aircraft tend to use kgs and metres.

EXAMPLE

BASIC(EMPTY) WEIGHT	Aircraft G-AAAA From the weight schedule for G-AAAA the weight is 1156.7 lbs.
VARIABLE LOAD	Pilot 155 lbs
DISPOSABLE LOAD	Passenger 150 lbs Full Useable Fuel (22.5 US gal) 135 lbs

From these figures a table can be made up to check weight and balance, remembering that moment is calculated by lever arm X weight.

ITEM	WEIGHT (lbs)	LEVER ARM	MOMENT
BASIC (EMPTY) WEIGHT - the basic weight, and its moment, are listed in the weight schedule			
for G-AAAA	1156.7	32.28	37345
VARIABLE LOAD Pilot	155	38.5	5967.5
DISPOSABLE LOAD Passenger	150	38.5	5775
Full (useable) fuel	135	41.5	5602.5
TOTAL WEIGHT 1596.7		TOTAL MOMENT 54690	

By totalling the weights you can see that the weight is below the maximum permitted (1600 lbs) - just!

If total moment is divided by total weight, the CG position will result

$$\frac{54690}{1596.7} = 34.25 \text{ inches aft of datum}$$

From the fore and aft c.g. limits given in the weight schedule, it will be seen that the aircraft IS loaded within its cg position limits.

Alternatively the total weight and TOTAL moment can be plotted on the centre of gravity moment envelope in the aircraft flight manual.

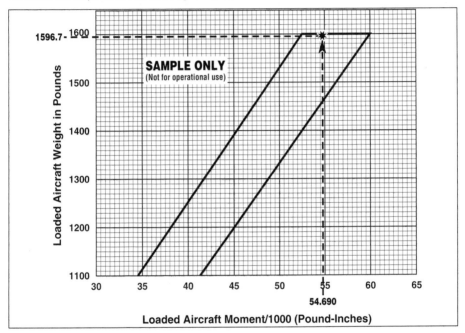

As you can see - the aircraft is loaded within limits.

NOTE: Some F150 flight manuals have an error in the centre of gravity moment envelope, in that the maximum weight shown is incorrect. Check carefully that the maximum weight shown in the flight manual you are using is correct - ie 726Kg/1600lbs.

Remember that differing flight manuals and differing weight schedules may use different units (ie metres or inches, lbs or kg etc). Always be absolutely clear which units you are working in. The figures given in the examples are NOT to be used operationally, although the principle of calculating aircraft loading remains the same.

Use of the Loading Graph

The mathematical calculation of weight and balance does give a very accurate answer, but it can be laborious to calculate - especially if you don't have a calculator!

Where the aircraft flight manual includes a loading graph, this can be used to calculate the moment for each item of loading - you don't even need to know the lever arm. We will use the figures from the preceding example. The moment for the basic weight is taken from the weight schedule.

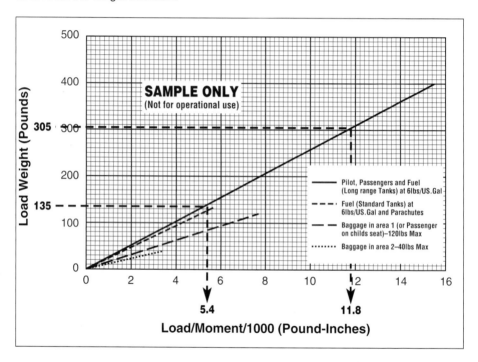

The figures derived from the loading graph can be put into a simplified table:

	Wt(lbs)	Moment/1000(lb/ins)
Basic (empty) weight	1156.7	37
Pilot & Passenger	305	11.8
Full useable fuel	135	5.4
	1596.7	54.2

Again the weight is checked first to ensure it is below the maximum permitted.

As the weight is below the maximum, the total weight and total moment can be plotted on the centre of gravity moment envelope in the flight manual to check balance.

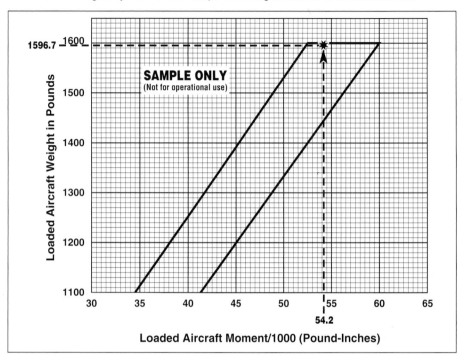

As you can see, the loading is within limits. The loading graph gives a quicker calculation of loading, at the expense of a slightly less accurate answer. If the loading is very close to the edge of the centre of gravity envelope it is worth using the mathematical method of loading calculation to get an exact cg position.

A WORD OF WARNING. As well as the safety aspect, operating the aircraft outside its weight and balance envelope has far reaching legal and financial implications. Almost the first thing an accident investigator will check after an accident is the loading of the aircraft. If the loading is outside limits the pilot is contravening the Air Navigation Order. In addition both the aircraft insurance company and your personal insurance company will be unsympathetic when they know that the conditions of the Certificate of Airworthiness (ie the flight manual limitations) were not complied with. As the pilot in command the responsibility is yours alone. The fact that the aircraft has two seats does not necessarily mean that the aircraft can be flown with both seats occupied, baggage and full fuel load.

C150 Loading Graph

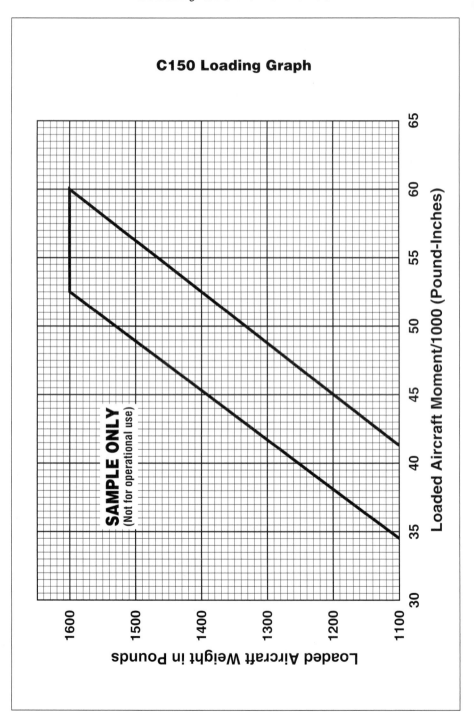

SAMPLE ONLY
(Not for operational use)

Loaded Aircraft Moment/1000 (Pound-Inches)

Loaded Aircraft Weight in Pounds

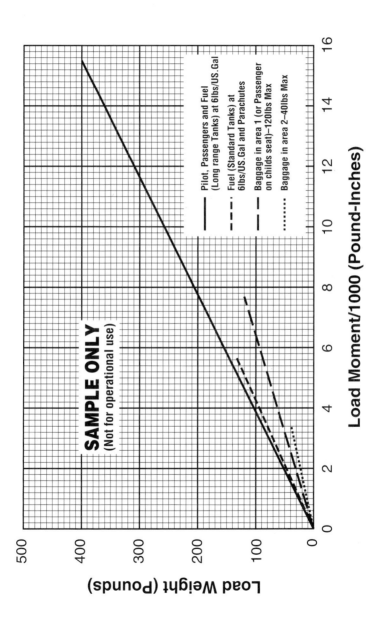

C150 Centre of Gravity Moment Envelope

SAMPLE ONLY
(Not for operational use)

Legend:
— Pilot, Passengers and Fuel (Long range Tanks) at 6lbs/US.Gal
–·– Fuel (Standard Tanks) at 6lbs/US.Gal and Parachutes
– – Baggage in area 1 (or Passenger on childs seat)–120lbs Max
······ Baggage in area 2–40lbs Max

Load Moment/1000 (Pound-Inches)

Load Weight (Pounds)

Performance

Generally the performance data found in a C150 flight manual is pretty basic.

The most commonly required data are the take-off and landing distances, and it is the calculation of these we will concentrate on here. To allow for variations not covered in the flight manual we will make use of the take-off and landing distance factors set out in section 7 (pages 7.1 and 7.2).

When calculating take-off and landing distances you should appreciate two very important points. Firstly the given performance will have been achieved using the specified techniques - check in the flight manual to see what the recommended techniques are. Secondly, you can safely assume that the flight manual results have been obtained by placing a brand-new aircraft in the hands of an experienced test pilot. It doesn't take too much thought to realise that as the last C150 was built in 1977, the average 150 has to be at least 20 years old. No-one would expect a 20 year old car to perform as well as it did when brand new; and no matter how well maintained, in the real world a 150's performance is bound to deteriorate over the years. Furthermore, the real world contains few experienced test pilots flying in ideal conditions (and even fewer flying C-150s!). It stands to reason you are not likely to achieve precisely the take off or landing distances given in the flight manual.

To make allowances for the "real-world" factor, it is wise to add a safety factor to the distances you calculate. Public transport operations are subject to an overall factoring of 1.33 for take offs and 1.43 for landings. It is highly recommended that the pilot apply the same factor to any table figures ie a calculated take off distance of 500 meters becomes 500 X 1.33 = 665 meters. As with loading calculations the pilot must use the tables and data from the documents for the individual aircraft being used. The tables and diagrams used in this section are for illustrative purposes only and NOT for operational use.

In section 7 various conversion factors are listed, together with recommended factors for variations not necessarily covered by the flight manual tables.

C-150 Take-off and Landing Performance Tables

The take-off and landing distance tables in the flight manual make several assumptions (eg paved level dry runway; use of flight manual technique etc).

The tables use the term "Pressure Altitude". This is the altitude of the runway assuming standard pressure setting (ie 1013 mb - or 1013 hPa if you prefer). When the QNH is other than 1013 you will need to adjust the actual altitude to get the pressure altitude. At the aircraft this can be done by simply setting the altimeter to 1013 and taking the indicated altitude. Without an altimeter handy adjust the actual altitude by 30' for each millibar/hectopascal above or below 1013. Remember when the QNH is above 1013 the pressure altitude is less than actual, and vice versa.

The headwind or tailwind component is calculated from the windspeed and angle of wind direction to the runway, (eg a 10 knot wind directly down the runway gives a headwind component of 10 knots; a 10 knot wind at 90° gives a headwind component of zero). There is a graph in section 7 for calculation of head/tailwind component and crosswind component.

The take-off and landing distance tables will contain a reminder to check the flight manual recommended technique. To get the flight manual results you must use the flight manual technique.

Take off Performance

The take off performance can be divided into two sections:

The TAKE OFF RUN (or Take Off Ground Roll), the distance taken for the aircraft to become airborne, and;

The TAKE OFF DISTANCE, that is the total distance required for the aircraft to become airborne AND clear a 50' barrier.

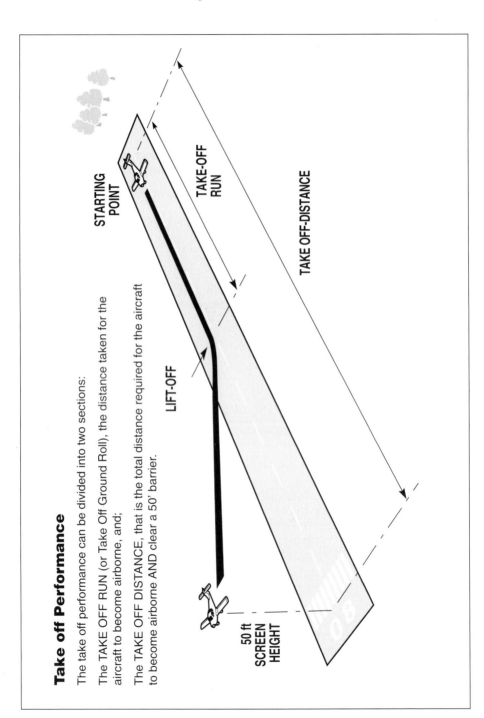

STARTING
POINT

TAKE-OFF
RUN

TAKE OFF-DISTANCE

LIFT-OFF

50 ft
SCREEN
HEIGHT

Take-off Distance Calculation Example

For the example we will take the conditions as:

Outside air temperature +20°C

Pressure Altitude 1000'

Dry level paved runway

Firstly, the closest conditions to those above are used to extract a baseline figure. Using sea level pressure altitude and +15°C gives a figure of 1385'.

TAKE - OFF DISTANCE FLAPS RETRACTED –

GROSS WEIGHT LBS.	IAS 50 FT. MPH	HEAD WIND KNOTS	AT SEA LEVEL & 15°C/59°F		AT 2500 FT. & 10°C/50°F.		AT 5000 FT.
			GROUND RUN	TOTAL TO CLEAR 50 FT. OBS.	GROUND RUN	TOTAL TO CLEAR 50 FT. OBS.	GROUND RUN
		0	735	1385	910	1660	1115
1600	70	10	500	1035	630	1250	780
		20	305	730	395	890	505

NOTES
1. Increase the distances 10% for each 35°f. increase in temperature above standard for the p
2. For operation on a dry, grass runway, increase distances (both "ground run" and "total to cl "total to clear 50 ft. obstacle" figure.

The actual pressure altitude is 1000', so using the table at page 7.1, a 10% increase in take-off distance is calculated; 1385 X 1.1 = 1524'. Temperature is +20°C, ie 5°C above that used in the flight manual. The table on page 7.1 recommends a factor of 10% increase for each 10°C increase in temperature, so it is safe to allow a 5% increase in take-off distance for a 5°C increase in temperature; 1524 X 1.05 = 1600'.

Finally this figure is multiplied by the take-off distance safety factor (1.33); so the take-off distance required is 1600' X 1.33 = 2128' or 649m.

NOTE: Some aircraft have a CAA supplement calling for a % increase in calculated distances due to performance shortfalls discovered during flight tests. Check if such a supplement applies to the aircraft you are flying.

Landing Performance

The landing performance is calculated as the LANDING DISTANCE, that is the total distance from 50' over the runway to a full stop. The ground roll (or ground run) - the distance from touch down to full stop may also be calculated.

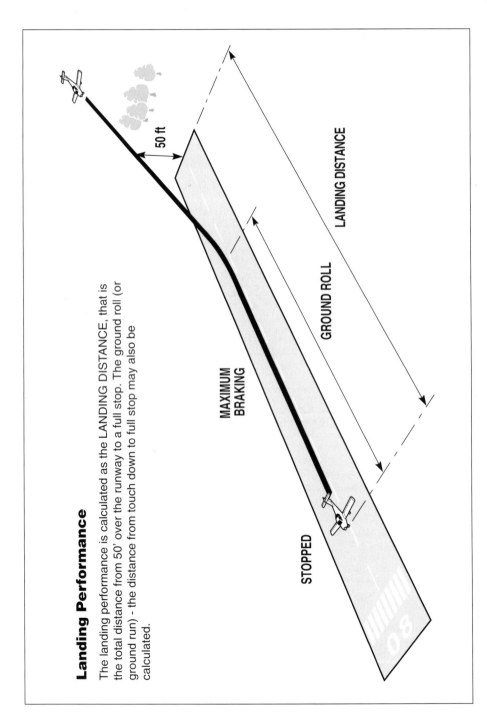

50 ft

MAXIMUM
BRAKING

STOPPED

GROUND ROLL

LANDING DISTANCE

08

Landing Distance Calculation Example

For this example we will take the conditions as:

Outside air temperature +15°C

Pressure altitude 1000'

Dry level paved runway

Headwind component 10 knots

		AT SEA LEVEL & 15°C/59°F		AT 2500 FT. & 10°C/50°F.		AT 5000 FT.
GROSS WEIGHT LBS.	APPROACH SPEED, IAS, MPH	GROUND ROLL	TOTAL TO CLEAR 50 FT. OBS.	GROUND ROLL	TOTAL TO CLEAR 50 FT. OBS.	GROUND ROLL
1600	60	445	1075	470	1135	495

LANDING DISTANCE — FLAPS LOWERED, HARD SURFACE F

NOTES
1. Decrease the distances shown by 10% for each 4 knots of headwind.
2. Increase the distance by 10% for each 60°F. temperature increase above standard.
3. For operation on a dry, grass runway, increase distances (both "ground roll" and "total to c the "total to clear 50 ft. obstacle" figure.

The calculation technique is much the same as for the take-off distance calculation. Using the closest parameters on the table (sea level pressure altitude and +15°C) gives a base line figure of 1075'.

This figure is increased by 5% to allow for the 1000' increase in pressure altitude (see page 7.2); 1075 X 1.05 = 1129'. The flight manual states that landing distance is reduced by 10% for each 4 knots of headwind component, so given 10 knots of headwind component:

$$\frac{10}{4} \quad X \quad 10\% \quad = \quad 25\%$$

When 1129' is reduced by 25%, the landing distance becomes 847'. Finally this figure is multiplied by the landing distance safety margin (1.43) to get the actual landing distance required:

$$847 \quad X \quad 1.43 \quad = \quad 1211' \text{ or } 369m$$

Enroute Performance

The flight manual may also have tables to calculate cruise performance.
It is wise to factor the cruise performance figures by at least 10% (ie increase fuel consumption by 10%), and remember the figures are based on the use of the flight manual recommended mixture leaning procedure. If you do not use this recommended procedure you are unlikely to achieve the table figures.

It is also necessary to allow an adequate fuel margin - say not less than 45 mins fuel reserve on landing. The infinite number of variables that can effect any flight (eg stronger than forecast headwinds, change of routing, higher than expected fuel consumption, delay at holding point prior to departure etc) make it foolhardy to attempt to fly to the very limit of calculated range or endurance.

TAKE - OFF DISTANCE

FLAPS RETRACTED – HARD SURFACE RUNWAY

GROSS WEIGHT LBS.	IAS 50 FT. MPH	HEAD WIND KNOTS	AT SEA LEVEL & 15°C/59°F		AT 2500 FT. & 10°C/50°F.		AT 5000 FT. & 5°C/41°F.		AT 7500 FT. & 0°C/32°F.	
			GROUND RUN	TOTAL TO CLEAR 50 FT. OBS.	GROUND RUN	TOTAL TO CLEAR 50 FT. OBS.	GROUND RUN	TOTAL TO CLEAR 50 FT. OBS.	GROUND RUN	TOTAL TO CLEAR 50 FT. OBS.
1600	70	0	735	1385	910	1660	1115	1985	1360	2440
		10	500	1035	630	1250	780	1510	970	1875
		20	305	730	395	890	505	1090	640	1375

NOTES
1. Increase the distances 10% for each 35°f. increase in temperature above standard for the particular altitude.
2. For operation on a dry, grass runway, increase distances (both "ground run" and "total to clear 50 ft. obstacle") by 7% of the "total to clear 50 ft. obstacle" figure.

LANDING DISTANCE

**FLAPS LOWERED TO 40° – POWER OFF
HARD SURFACE RUNWAY – ZERO WIND**

GROSS WEIGHT LBS.	APPROACH SPEED, IAS, MPH	AT SEA LEVEL & 15°C/59°F		AT 2500 FT. & 10°C/50°F.		AT 5000 FT. & 5°C/41°F.		AT 7500 FT. & 0°C/32°F.	
		GROUND ROLL	TOTAL TO CLEAR 50 FT. OBS.	GROUND ROLL	TOTAL TO CLEAR 50 FT. OBS.	GROUND ROLL	TOTAL TO CLEAR 50 FT. OBS.	GROUND ROLL	TOTAL TO CLEAR 50 FT. OBS.
1600	60	445	1075	470	1135	495	1195	520	1255

NOTES
1. Decrease the distances shown by 10% for each 4 knots of headwind.
2. Increase the distance by 10% for each 60°F. temperature increase above standard.
3. For operation on a dry, grass runway, increase distances (both "ground roll" and "total to clear 50 ft. obstacle") by 20% of the "total to clear 50 ft. obstacle" figure.

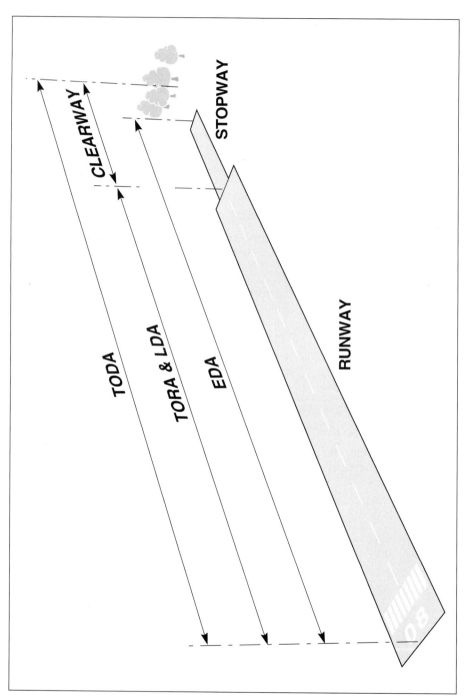

Runway Dimensions

Having calculated the distances the aircraft requires for take off or landing, the runway dimensions must be checked to ensure that the aircraft can be safely operated on the runway in question. The figures given in the AIP or airfield guide can be defined in a number of ways.

The Take Off Run Available (TORA)

The TORA is the length of the runway available for the take off ground run of the aircraft. This is usually the physical length of the runway.

The Emergency Distance (ED)

The ED is the length of the TORA plus the length of any stopway. A stopway is an area at the end of the TORA prepared for an aircraft to stop on in the event of an abandoned take off. The ED is also known as the

ACCELERATE - STOP DISTANCE AVAILABLE.

The Take Off Distance Available (TODA)

The TODA is the TORA plus the length of any clearway. A clearway is an area over which an aircraft may make its initial climb (to 50' in this instance). The TODA will not be more than 1.5 X TORA.

The Landing Distance Available (LDA)

The LDA is the length of the runway available for the ground run of an aircraft landing. In all cases the landing distance required should never be greater than the landing distance available.

The Cessna 150

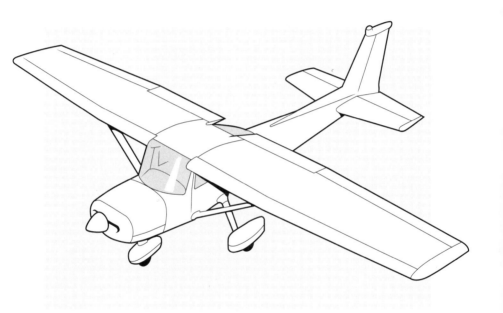

Conversions

Take-off Distance Factors

The following factors will allow the pilot to make allowance for variations that may effect take-off performance. Although some of these factors are covered in the C150 performance graphs, the graph is produced in its entirety for completeness:

VARIATION	INCREASE IN TAKE-OFF DISTANCE (to 50')	FACTOR
10% increase in aircraft weight	20%	**1.2**
Increase of 1000' in runway altitude	10%	**1.1**
Increase in temperature of 10°C	10%	**1.1**
Dry Grass		
- Short (under 5 inches)	20%	**1.2**
- Long (5 - 10 inches)	25%	**1.25**
Wet Grass		
- Short	25%	**1.25**
- Long	30%	**1.3**
2% uphill slope	10%	**1.1**
Tailwind component of 10% of lift off speed	20%	**1.2**
Soft ground or snow *	at least 25%	**at least 1.25**

* snow and other runway contamination is covered on page 7.3.

Landing Distance Factors

The following factors will allow the pilot to make allowance for variations that may effect landing performance. Although some of these factors are covered in the C150 performance graphs, the graph is produced in its entirety for completeness:

VARIATION	INCREASE IN LANDING DISTANCE (from 50')	FACTOR
10% increase in aircraft weight	10%	**1.1**
Increase of 1000' in runway altitude	5%	**1.05**
Increase in temperature of 10°C	5%	**1.05**
Dry Grass		
- Short (under 5 inches)	20%	**1.2**
- Long (5 - 10 inches)	30%	**1.3**
Wet Grass		
- Short	30%	**1.30**
- Long	40%	**1.40**
2% downhill slope	10%	**1.1**
Tailwind component of 10% of landing speed	20%	**1.2**
snow *	at least 25%	**at least 1.25**

* snow and other runway contamination is covered on page 7.3.

Runway Contamination

A runway can be contaminated by water, snow or slush. If operation on such a runway cannot be avoided additional allowance must be made for the problems such contamination may cause - ie additional drag, reduced braking performance (possible aquaplaning), and directional control problems.

It is generally recommended that take-off should not be attempted if dry snow covers the runway to a depth of more than 60mm, or if water, slush or wet snow covers the runway to more than 15mm. In addition a tailwind, or crosswind component exceeding 10 knots should not be accepted when operating on a slippery runway.

For take-off distance required calculations the other known conditions should be factored, and the emergency distance available on the runway should be at least 2.0 X the take-off distance required (for a paved runway) or at least 2.66 X the take-off distance required (for a grass runway).

When landing any water or slush can have a very adverse effect on landing performance, and the danger of aquaplaning (with negligible wheel braking and loss of directional control) is very real.

Use of the Wind Component Graph

This graph can be used to find the head/tail wind component and the crosswind component, given a particular wind velocity and runway direction.

EXAMPLE:

Runway 27

Surface wind 240°/15 knots

The angle between the runway direction (270°) and wind direction(240°) is 30°. Now on the graph locate a point on the 30° line, where it crosses the 15 knot arc. From this point take a horizontal line to give the headwind component (13 knots) and a vertical line to give the crosswind component (8 knots).

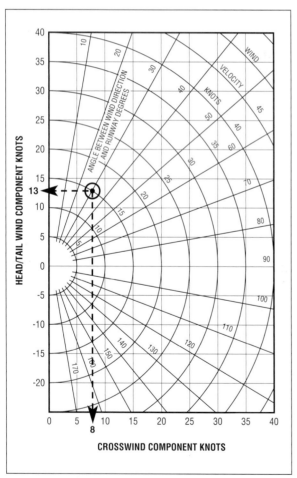

On the main graph overleaf the shaded area represents the maximum demonstrated crosswind component for the F-150M. If the wind point is within this shaded area, the maximum demonstrated crosswind component for this aircraft has been exceeded.

Note: Runway direction will be degrees magnetic. Check the wind direction given is also in degrees magnetic.

Wind Component Graph

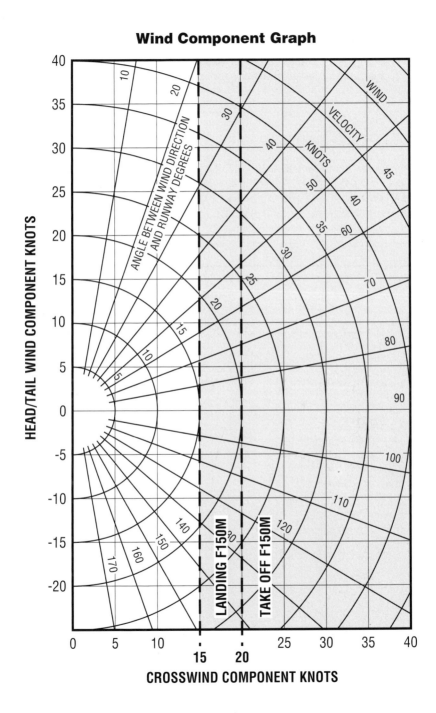

Conversions

TEMPERATURE

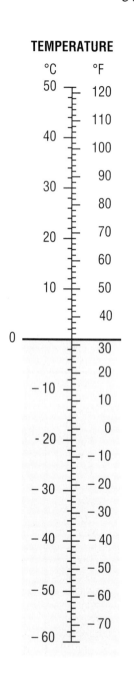

PRESSURE

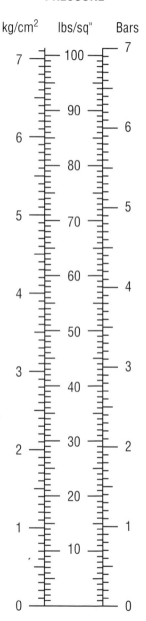

Distance-Metres/Feet

Metres	Feet		Feet	Metres
1	3.28		1	0.30
2	6.56		2	0.61
3	9.84		3	0.91
4	13.12		4	1.22
5	16.40		5	1.52
6	19.69		6	1.83
7	22.97		7	2.13
8	26.25		8	2.44
9	29.53		9	2.74
10	32.81		10	3.05
20	65.62		20	6.10
30	98.43		30	9.14
40	131.23		40	12.19
50	164.04		50	15.24
60	196.85		60	18.29
70	229.66		70	21.34
80	262.47		80	24.38
90	295.28		90	27.43
100	328.08		100	30.48
200	656.16		200	60.96
300	984.25		300	91.44
400	1,312.34		400	121.92
500	1,640.42		500	152.40
600	1,968.50		600	182.88
700	2,296.59		700	213.36
800	2,624.67		800	243.84
900	2,952.76		900	274.32
1000	3,280.84		1000	304.80
2000	6,561.70		2000	609.60
3000	9,842.50		3000	914.40
4000	13.123.40		4000	1,219.20
5000	16,404.20		5000	1,524.00
6000	19,685.00		6000	1,828.80
7000	22,965.90		7000	2,133.60
8000	26,246.70		8000	2,438.40
9000	29,527.60		9000	2,743.20
10000	32,808.40		10000	3,048.00

Conversion Factors:

Centimetres to Inches x .3937
Inches to Centimetres x 2.54

Metres to Feet x 3.28084
Feet to Metres x 0.3048

Distance-KM/Nautical Miles/Statute Miles

NM	Km	St		Km	NM	St		ST	NM	Km
1	1.85	1.15		1	.54	.62		1	.87	1.61
2	3.70	2.30		2	1.08	1.24		2	1.74	3.22
3	5.56	3.45		3	1.62	1.86		3	2.61	4.83
4	7.41	4.60		4	2.16	2.49		4	3.48	6.44
5	9.26	5.75		5	2.70	3.11		5	4.34	8.05
6	11.11	6.90		6	3.24	3.73		6	5.21	9.66
7	12.96	8.06		7	3.78	4.35		7	6.08	11.27
8	14.82	9.21		8	4.32	4.97		8	6.95	12.87
9	16.67	10.36		9	4.86	5.59		9	7.82	14.48
10	18.52	11.51		10	5.40	6.21		10	8.69	16.09
20	37.04	23.02		20	10.80	12.43		20	17.38	32.19
30	55.56	34.52		30	16.20	18.64		30	26.07	48.28
40	74.08	46.03		40	21.60	24.86		40	34.76	64.37
50	92.60	57.54		50	27.00	31.07		50	43.45	80.47
60	111.12	69.05		60	32.40	37.28		60	52.14	96.56
70	129.64	80.55		70	37.80	43.50		70	60.83	112.65
80	148.16	92.06		80	43.20	49.71		80	69.52	128.75
90	166.68	103.57		90	48.60	55.92		90	78.21	144.84
100	185.2	115.1		100	54.0	62.1		100	86.9	161.0
200	370.4	230.2		200	108.0	124.3		200	173.8	321.9
300	555.6	345.2		300	162.0	186.4		300	260.7	482.8
400	740.8	460.3		400	216.0	248.6		400	347.6	643.7
500	926.0	575.4		500	270.0	310.7		500	434.5	804.7
600	1111.2	690.5		600	324.0	372.8		600	521.4	965.6
700	1296.4	805.6		700	378.0	435.0		700	608.3	1126.5
800	1481.6	920.6		800	432.0	497.1		800	695.2	1287.5
900	1666.8	1035.7		900	486.0	559.2		900	782.1	1448.4

Conversion Factors:

Statute Miles to Nautical Miles x 0.868976
Statute Miles to Kilometres x 1.60934
Kilometres to Statute Miles x 0.62137
Kilometres to Nautical Miles x 0.539957
Nautical Miles to Statute Miles x 1.15078
Nautical Miles to Kilometres x 1.852

Weight

lbs	Kg	Kg	lbs
1	.45	1	2.20
2	.91	2	4.41
3	1.38	3	6.61
4	1.81	4	8.82
5	2.27	5	11.02
6	2.72	6	13.23
7	3.18	7	15.43
8	3.63	8	17.64
9	4.08	9	19.84
10	4.54	10	22.05
20	9.07	20	44.09
30	13.61	30	66.14
40	18.14	40	88.18
50	22.68	50	110.23
60	27.22	60	132.28
70	31.75	70	154.32
80	36.29	80	176.37
90	40.82	90	198.42
100	45.4	100	220.5
200	90.7	200	440.9
300	136.1	300	661.4
400	181.4	400	881.8
500	226.8	500	1102.3
600	272.2	600	1322.8
700	317.5	700	1543.2
800	362.9	800	1763.7
900	408.2	900	1984.2
1000	453.6	1000	2204.6
2000	907.2	2000	4409.2
3000	1360.8	3000	6613.9
4000	1814.4	4000	8818.5
5000	2268.0	5000	11023.1
6000	2721.5	6000	13227.7
7000	3175.1	7000	15432.3
8000	3628.7	8000	17637.0
9000	4082.3	9000	19841.6
10000	4535.9	10000	22046.2

Conversion Factors:

lbs to Kilograms x 0.45359
Kilograms to lbs x 2.20462

Volume (Fluid)

Litres	Imp. Gall	U.S. Gall	U.S. Gall	Imp. Gall	Litres	Imp. Gall	U.S. Gall	Litres
1	0.22	0.26	1	0.83	3.79	1	1.20	4.55
2	0.44	0.53	2	1.67	7.57	2	2.40	9.09
3	0.66	0.79	3	2.50	11.36	3	3.60	13.64
4	0.88	1.06	4	3.33	15.14	4	4.80	18.18
5	1.10	1.32	5	4.16	18.93	5	6.00	22.73
6	1.32	1.59	6	5.00	22.71	6	7.21	27.28
7	1.54	1.85	7	5.83	26.50	7	8.41	31.82
8	1.76	2.11	8	6.66	30.28	8	9.61	36.37
9	1.98	2.38	9	7.49	34.07	9	10.81	40.91
10	2.20	2.64	10	8.33	37.85	10	12.01	45.46
20	4.40	5.28	20	16.65	75.71	20	24.02	90.92
30	6.60	7.93	30	24.98	113.56	30	36.03	136.38
40	8.80	10.57	40	33.31	151.41	40	48.04	181.84
50	11.00	13.21	50	41.63	189.27	50	60.05	227.30
60	13.20	15.85	60	49.96	227.12	60	72.06	272.76
70	15.40	18.49	70	58.29	264.97	70	84.07	318.22
80	17.60	21.14	80	66.61	302.82	80	96.08	363.68
90	19.80	23.78	90	74.94	340.68	90	108.09	409.14
100	22.00	26.42	100	83.27	378.54	100	120.09	454.60
200	44.00	52.84						
300	66.00	79.26						
400	88.00	105.68						
500	110.00	132.10						
600	132.00	158.52						
700	154.00	184.94						
800	176.00	211.36						
900	198.00	237.78						
1000	220.00	264.20						

Conversion Factors:

Imperial Gallons to Litres x 4.54596
Litres to Imperial Gallons x 0.219975
U.S. Gallons to Litres x 3.78541
Litres to U.S. Gallons x 0.264179
Imperial Gallons to U.S. Gallons x 1.20095
U.S. Gallons to Imperial Gallons x 0.832674

C150 - Index

Index